THE SIZE OF THE UNIVERSE

UNIVERSE

F. J. HARGREAVES, F.R.A.S.

PENGUIN BOOKS

WEST DRAYTON · MIDDLESEX

Specially written for Pelican Books and first published 1948

Made and Printed in Great Britain for Penguin Books Ltd.
by Hunt, Barnard and Company Ltd., London and Aylesbury

CONTENTS

LIST OF PLATES

THE SIZE OF THE UNIVERSE:
HOW IT IS MEASURED

INTRODUCTION

EVERYONE has learnt something about the modern picture of the universe – its vast, unimaginable distances, its lifelessness, its indifference to and aloofness from mankind – so completely different from the primitive picture in which mankind is the centre and everything around, beneath and above him ministers to his needs. How has this enormous change in our outlook come about? What is the nature of the evidence for the modern view? These questions must have occurred to everyone at some time or other and many of the popular books on astronomy fail to answer them. All too often they merely present the conclusions and the reader is expected to accept them unquestioningly.

There has consequently appeared in recent years a somewhat reserved attitude to astronomy, in which there is an element of scepticism, coupled with a suspicion that the ordinary man's mind is not adequate to understand these high matters – or at least that the astronomers consider it to be inadequate, otherwise why do they so rarely attempt to explain?

There is no ground for this suspicion. The processes and arguments which have led to the modern view of the universe can be understood and appreciated by anyone capable of rational thinking, and when these arguments are appreciated it will be found that there is little room for scepticism. The aim of this book is to explain, in terms that everyone can follow, the methods that have been, and are being, used to explore and gauge the universe, the various lines of reasoning by which the facts of observation have been interpreted, the assumptions which underlie the reasoning and how, and to what extent, these assumptions have been tested and validated.

Every science uses a language of its own, and astronomy is

no exception. Technical terms, incomprehensible to laymen, must be used by practitioners of the science if only for the sake of brevity, but they have the unfortunate effect of erecting a barrier between the initiated and the uninitiated.

In this book technical terms are avoided as far as possible, and care has been taken to define and explain those that must be used. Much of the work of the astronomer is done in the language of mathematics, which is a sealed book to most people. Mathematics (other than simple arithmetic and geometry) is avoided altogether, and lavish use is made of simple graphical methods of deriving the results.

It should not be imagined that this book covers the whole subject of astronomy, which is far too vast to be expounded adequately in a single volume. There is nothing about positional astronomy, on which navigation depends, or astrophysics, which seeks to discover the physical nature, condition and composition of the stars, or descriptive astronomy, which deals with the appearance in the telescope of the planets and other bodies, or cosmogony which seeks to reveal the origin of the universe. For information about these branches of the subject other works must be consulted.

CHAPTER I

PRIMITIVE AND MODERN IDEAS CONTRASTED

NOWADAYS everyone is taught at school that the earth goes round the sun, that the other planets are bodies like the earth, going round the sun and shining by reflected sunlight, that the sun is about ninety million miles away and that the stars are immensely further away. It therefore requires a considerable effort to imagine how the visible universe would appear to anyone who had not been taught anything about it. Let us try.

His surroundings consist of a lower half in which everything is accessible and touchable and an upper half in which everything is out of reach and more remote than anything in the lower half – for the sun, the moon and the stars appear above and disappear beneath the horizon behind the furthest objects visible on the earth, and behind and above the highest clouds which cannot be reached even by climbing high mountains. On the summit of a mountain, above the lower clouds at least, these objects would not appear appreciably nearer. Remoteness, then, would be the first and outstanding impression.

The sun would appear to be supported in some inscrutable way by, or beneath, a vast blue dome, but it would not be possible to decide immediately whether this dome moved with the sun (in which case the sun would be fixed to it) or whether the sun travelled across the surface of a stationary dome. At any rate it would be perfectly obvious that the sun moved and the earth stayed still.

After sunset the blue of the sky would be seen to fade and change to black, spangled with bright points of light, which all wheel together in the same direction as the sun. There would be no doubt about these points of light – they are obviously carried by the black dome, and because at least part of this dome had just previously been blue, the inference would be that the dome is the same day and night, the blue being due to the light of the sun.

So much would be observable in a day and a night. Neglecting the moon for the time being, observations extending over a year or more would reveal further facts. The same stars are not visible throughout the year; a star which rises in the east about sunset at one time of the year is progressively higher in the sky at sunset as time passes, travelling westwards gradually and finally becoming lost in the west in the glare of the sun and remaining invisible for some months, until it is seen once again rising in the east at sunset.

Another conspicuous fact, of course, is that the sun's path across the sky is not the same from day to day; this path shifts gradually northwards and then southwards and then northwards again. It would be noticed that if a star rises at sunset when the sun is following its most northerly path (at midsummer in our part of the world) then the next time this star rises at sunset the sun would again be following its most northerly path. Observations extended over a great many years (several lifetimes would be necessary) would reveal that this is not quite accurate; but we need not concern ourselves with this.

Combining these facts, it would be possible to deduce that the sun travels slowly round the 'dome' (by this time recognised to be a complete sphere) from west to east, in a track inclined to the paths which are followed by the stars (and the sun) from east to west once a day. The stars would be regarded as fixed to the sphere, the visible half of which appears as a blue dome by day and a black dome by night. The sun, blotting out the stars when it is above the horizon and lighting up the blue surface of the sphere, would be pictured as moving slowly eastwards round the sphere along an inclined or tilted track.

The great majority of the stars would be seen to keep strictly to their relative position in the sky, clinching the idea that they are fixed to the sphere, but it would be noticed in time that five of them wander about among the others, and are distinguishable from them also by the fact that they do not twinkle. These five non-twinkling wanderers are therefore like the sun in that they move across the surface of the sphere. Moreover it would be noticed that their movements are confined to the same inclined track that the sun follows in the course of a year. Accurate observations show that this is not quite correct, but the departures which they make from this track, to the north or south, are not such as would be very noticeable to the naked eye.

Let us see how each of these wanderers or 'planets' behaves. One of them (Mercury) is never far away from the sun and therefore never looks very bright; sometimes it is seen in the evening, low down near the western horizon soon after sunset, and sometimes in the morning near the eastern horizon before sunrise. Another (Venus) is also seen only in the evening and in the early morning and never in the middle of the night. Like Mercury, it travels from one side of the sun to the other, but the distance which it attains from the sun, to the west and to the east, is much greater and it is incomparably brighter. In fact at times it is far brighter than any other star or planet.

It would be some time before it would be clear that the two planets seen in the evening were the same as those seen in the morning; the ancients had different names for Venus-in-the-evening and Venus-in-the-morning. Mercury also had two names.

The remaining three planets behave quite differently; each of them is visible from time to time in the middle of the night and each of them is due south at midnight at regular intervals. Mars, fiery red in colour, is due south at midnight (opposite to the sun, or 'in opposition' as the astronomers say) at intervals of about two years and two months. Jupiter, golden yellow, is in opposition at intervals of about thirteen months, and Saturn, also yellow but not so bright as Mars or Jupiter, at intervals of just over a year -- a year and thirteen days.

That these three planets, like Mercury and Venus, move along the inclined track of the sun is evident from the fact that when any one of them is in opposition, it is in the part of the sky that the sun occupied six months earlier, and will occupy six months later. In our part of the world, a planet in opposition in summer is low in the sky, and *vice versa*, when in opposition in the winter it is high in the sky. If opposition occurs in spring or autumn, the planet is at a medium altitude such as the sun occupies both in spring and in autumn.

The sun moves uniformly and regularly (not quite, but very nearly) around its inclined track, but these three planets (Mars, Jupiter and Saturn) do not. They sometimes move eastwards among the stars, like the sun. At times this motion ceases and they appear to be quite stationary for some days, after which they move westwards only to become stationary again and then resume their eastward motion; but the steadily marching sun overtakes them all in turn, as it does the stars.

The amount of the westward or retrograde motion is greatest for Mars, less for Jupiter and least of all for Saturn.

In course of time our inquisitive star-gazer would gather further facts. He would be able to count the number of days between successive returns of the sun to the same point among the stars (365 days), the number of days between successive appearances of Mercury as an evening object (116 days), and of Venus (584 days). He might also note that Mars returned to the same point among the stars in a little less than two years, Jupiter in about twelve years, and Saturn in about thirty years.

The moon is a very different kind of object. It is obviously a mottled ball, it obviously revolves from west to east round the earth, and it is obviously lit up by the sun, this fact accounting satisfactorily for its changes of shape as it circles the sky. It is quite easy, by naked-eye observation alone, to deduce that the moon is very much nearer to us than the sun, and this deduction must have been made at a very early date. During each lunation there are two days when the moon is exactly a half-moon – one side is round and the other is straight, as near as can be judged. When this occurs near either of the equinoxes – towards the end of March or the end of September – it can be seen at once that when the sun is setting (in the case of a waxing moon), or rising (in the case of a waning moon), the moon is due south. But at these times the sun rises due east and sets due west. Lines drawn from the observer's eye to the sun and to the moon are therefore at right angles to one another.

Now consider Figure 1, a diagram drawn on the assumption that the sun is only slightly further from the earth than the moon (or rather from the observer O). Obviously, if this were so, when the lines OS and OM are at right angles to one

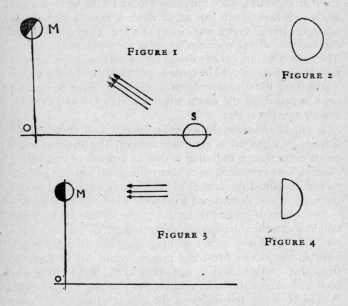

FIGURE 1

FIGURE 2

FIGURE 3

FIGURE 4

another, the moon is receiving light over the hemisphere shown white, some of which is to the left of the line joining O to the centre of the moon's disc. It would therefore appear to him gibbous, as in Figure 2. It does not look gibbous; it is like Figure 3, a half moon, and the corresponding diagram, Figure 4, puts the sun at a very great distance towards the right – many times as far as the moon.

It is interesting to speculate how long ago this simple

deduction was made, by what kind of man, and how his fellows received the information and his attempts to explain it. He probably had a hard time, judging from some analogous cases historically on record. The ancient Greeks were well aware of it, and they made an attempt to determine how many times further away the sun is than the moon by trying to observe how much the straight edge of the moon departed from straightness when the lines OS and OM were at right angles, or how much this angle differed from a right-angle when the straight edge was *exactly* straight. They decided that the sun was about nineteen times as far away as the moon. The correct number is 387 times, very nearly, and this number is so large that it would be quite hopeless to distinguish by the unaided eye the departure from straightness of the terminator (as it is called) of the moon when the lines OS and OM are exactly at right angles.

A single observer, however assiduous and acute, could scarcely be expected to get much further. The ancients knew much more than is indicated above, as a result of comparing observations extending over many lifetimes, but the general picture remained the same; only the details were filled in and the proportions determined with some approach to accuracy.

The reader is invited to try to ignore all that he has been taught about the solar system, to put himself in imagination in the place of this observer of long ago, and to ask himself whether the picture presented to him would differ materially from that outlined above, and whether he would have any reason to doubt the fixity and central position of the earth. Would he doubt the reality of the sphere to which the stars are attached? Would he doubt that the sun and moon, at least, were there solely to serve his needs and those of his fellows? As to the planets, can he be quite sure that he would be able to resist or question the suggestion that they are concerned with his own fortunes?

Surely it will be evident that a very great effort of imagination was required even to conceive that there could be an alternative to this earth-centred scheme of things, and still more to assert that the solid earth was only a planet, one of a family of six dancing attendance upon the central sun.

We know now that this is certainly so, and we also know that the wheeling sphere spangled with points of light is an illusion. We know that the sun is merely one of the stars, that some of them are immensely larger than the sun, which is itself nothing but an average, common sort of star whose fellows can be found in thousands of millions throughout the universe. We know that the distances between the stars are almost incomparably greater than those between the planets and the sun, that in contemplating even our own system of stars (one of many, many millions of such systems) our home, the earth, shrinks to an inconsiderable speck, a grain of dust, a mere mote. We know some of these distances as accurately almost as we know the distance between London and Edinburgh. We have a comprehensive general idea of the structure of the universe and its scale to distances which light takes two or three hundred million years to traverse – and we can be sure that our estimates of these distances are of the right order of magnitude.

The contrast between the old, primitive picture and the new is striking, to say the least, and it must be a matter of interest to every thoughtful person to trace the steps by which this tremendous transformation in our outlook has come about.

The essential first step was the establishment of the fact that the earth is one of the planets and, like them, revolves round the sun. It cannot be emphasised too strongly that this could not be proved beyond argument until the invention of the telescope and the power which it conferred on us of discovering the nature of the planets had enabled us to *put the question to the test of observation* – the scientific test.

A few words about the scientific method will not be out of place. There is really nothing mysterious or odd, or even very specialised, about it. Rational men have always used it and relied on it from the beginning – and still do, every hour of every day. Every time we say 'Let us go and see,' or, 'Let us try it and see' we are employing the scientific method. A man may say 'I wonder if this stuff would dissolve in water.' The reasonable response would be, 'Well, here's some water, let us see if it will,' – and we find out. We are establishing a fact by experiment. Or he may say to another, 'I believe it's raining.' The other replies, 'Oh! I don't think it is.' They either leave it at that, if they are not very interested, or, if the matter is of any importance to them they *go and see* if it is raining or not. They establish a fact by observation. Essentially there is no difference between their procedure and that of the first observer with a telescope, who looked at the heavenly bodies with a telescope and settled once for all the nature of the solar system.

The truth is that in ordinary, everyday matters, men have always employed the scientific method. It is the extension of this familiar method to things that are *not* ordinary, everyday matters which is labelled 'science'. The word, after all, only means knowledge – knowledge of whether it is raining or not at a particular place and time, knowledge of whether or not a substance will dissolve in water, whether or not wood will float in water, whether or not Venus revolves round the sun, whether or not matter is continuous or discontinuous in structure, and so on. All such knowledge is obtained by *observation* or *experiment* – by looking (or listening, tasting, feeling, smelling – whichever is appropriate) or by trying.

What should we think of two men who, instead of going to the door to see if it is raining, sit down and argue the matter for hours on end, by reference to what is written in the works of Plato, or Aristotle, or the Hebrew prophets? Yet that is what so-called philosophers did for centuries in this question of the rival geocentric (earth-centred) and heliocentric (sun-centred) systems. But we must resist the temptation to laugh at them. It is true that they argued interminably and comically about things that could have been settled in a moment by observation or experiment, but in this matter of the planets there was no such way of settling the controversy; naked-eye observations were not adequate.

This excuse lost its validity when Galileo Galilei for the

first time (in 1609) looked at the night sky through a telescope. He could say, 'Come and see for yourself.' Many refused, and one can only speculate about the state of their minds. It may be that they felt that to be certain about it would spoil their fun – the fun that some people, even in our own day, derive from argument for argument's sake.

The best attempt to explain the motions of the planets and

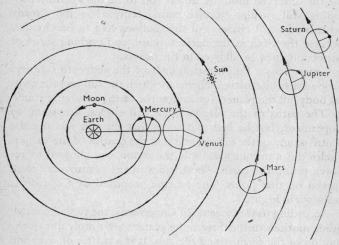

FIGURE 5

the sun on the basis of a fixed earth was made by Claudius Ptolemaeus (Ptolemy for short) in the second century A.D. His system is shown in Figure 5. The earth (by that time known to be a round globe, and to be rotating on its axis), is at the centre and all the other bodies revolve round it from west to east at different distances. The sun and moon move steadily and continuously. To account for the periodic retrograde, or westward, movements of the planets they were supposed to revolve in small circles, the *centres* of which moved steadily eastwards, like the sun. Mercury and Venus were no different from the other three in this respect, but the steadily-moving centres round which these two revolved always remained on the straight line connecting the earth with the sun. On this scheme they never went *behind* the sun – they always remained between the earth and the sun.

As observations became more and more accurate it was found that this simple scheme would not account completely for the observed motions, and it had to be modified by providing still smaller circular paths, centred on the already postulated small circles. All the motions had to be circular, because the circle is the perfect figure, and nothing short of perfection must be allowed in the heavens!

Copernicus, a Polish astronomer of the sixteenth century, proposed an alternative scheme in which the sun was the central body, all the planets (including the earth) revolving round it. The paths of the planets were still circles, according to Copernicus, but he had to assume that the sun was not the centre of any of the circles, and that the centres of the various circles did not coincide. Only the moon was allowed to revolve round the earth – both sides in the controversy were agreed on that point. The scheme proposed by Copernicus is shown in Figure 6.

According to this scheme of Copernicus, the periodic retrograde motions of the three outer planets are simply due to the motion of the earth round the sun. It is a matter of common experience that if, when one is looking at an object near to us, one moves one's head to the left, the object *appears* to move to the right across the far-distant background. The reader can verify this in a moment by looking at a bar of the window-frame, a lamp-post, or anything close at hand that happens to be in view, and moving his head sideways. This apparent movement of near objects across the background, due to the observer's own motion, is called *parallax* by astronomers. This word will be used frequently in the ensuing chapters. It is a technical expression, it is true, but it conveniently and briefly labels something which is one of the commonplaces of life – something so familiar that one almost feels it necessary to apologise for saying so much about it.

If the head is moved first to the left and then to the right, the object will appear to move first to the right and then to the left – another statement of the obvious. If the object is moving steadily from right to left, alternate movements of the head from side to side will make the object appear to move first

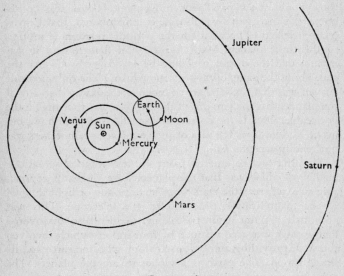

FIGURE 6

quickly, and through a considerable distance, to the right, and then slowly, and through a shorter distance, to the left, and so on alternately.

This is just what the outer planets appear to do, and Copernicus pointed out that that is what they would do if they moved steadily and uniformly in their orbits while we, on the earth, moved from side to side by reason of the earth's revolution round the sun once a year.

We must agree that in those days such a scheme would be difficult to accept. Much has been written about the arguments that were used by the two sides in the controversy and the part played by the Church, but for our present purpose we need only refer to one argument against the idea of a moving earth – the very reasonable argument that if the earth moved, its motion would be 'reflected' in the stars, which would oscillate from side to side of a mean position. In technical language they would show parallactic movement. It was this consequence of the earth's motion, be it remembered, that Copernicus invoked to account for the periodic retrograde motion of the three planets Mars, Jupiter and Saturn, and it was natural that the question should be asked – why do not the stars show the same oscillatory movement? The only possible answer was that the stars are so much farther away than any of the planets that the amount of the parallax was too small to be noticeable. This is the correct answer, as we now know, but in the Middle Ages the idea of such enormous remoteness was not readily acceptable.

The first fact to emerge from the telescopic observations made by Galileo was that the planets were globes of appreciable size, whereas the stars were mere points of light in spite of the magnification provided by the telescope. This was obviously a point against Ptolemy. Galileo also discovered that Jupiter was accompanied by four moons which revolved round it, providing an obvious analogy with the earth and its single moon. The earth is a globe; so are the planets. The earth has a moon revolving round it; Jupiter has four moons revolving round it. The inference therefore is that the earth is a sixth planet.

These facts, and this inference, made it highly probable that all six planets revolve round the sun, but it was still possible for the opponents of Copernicus to say that there was no definite proof – the earth, though similar in its nature to the planets, might well be unique among them as being the centre of the motions of all the rest.

The observations that clinched the matter were of Venus.

Galileo found that Venus showed a succession of phases exactly like those of the moon – full, gibbous, half or D-shaped, and crescent.

The decisive nature of this fact is seen in Figures 7 and 8. Figure 7 shows the orbit of Venus according to Ptolemy. Venus is shown in four positions, numbered 1, 2, 3, 4. When it is in positions 1 and 3 its dark side is turned towards the

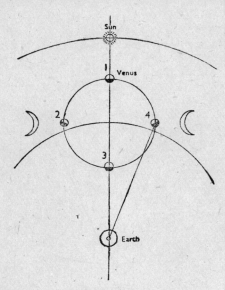

FIGURE 7

earth and it is therefore invisible. In positions 2 and 4 only a small part of the sunlit half of the planet is visible – it will look like the crescent moon, as shown on a larger scale at the sides of the figure. It could not look any 'larger' than this at any point in its orbit; it would always be a narrow crescent when visible at all.

Figure 8 shows the orbit according to Copernicus. When Venus is near position 1 its sunlit half will be turned towards the earth and it will appear nearly circular, like the moon near the full phase. At position 3 it will present its dark side towards the earth and will be invisible – unless, indeed, it crosses the face of the sun, when it will appear as a black spot on the sun. At positions 2 and 4, where it appears furthest away from the sun, it will be a half 'moon' – dichotomised

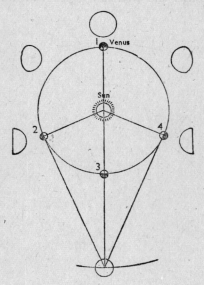

FIGURE 8

(cut in half) as the astronomers say. Obviously in positions between 1 and 2, or between 1 and 4, it will appear gibbous, while between 2 and 3, or 3 and 4, it will be a crescent, narrower in proportion as it is closer to position 3.

Galileo saw, with the aid of his telescope, that the phases of Venus were like those of Figure 8, not like those of Figure 7. This was proof that Venus revolves round the sun, and not round a point (between earth and sun) revolving round the earth, as taught by Ptolemy. His telescope was not adequate to reveal that Mercury showed the same succession of phases as Venus, Mercury being smaller, and further from the earth, than Venus. His successors, however, with more powerful telescopes, soon found that this was so, and therefore that Mercury too revolved round the sun.

What of the remaining three planets? A comparison of Figures 5 and 6 will show at once that the succession of phases will be the same in both schemes. Neither Mars nor Jupiter nor Saturn will ever appear dichotomised, much less crescentic; when farthest from the sun in the sky they will appear gibbous, Saturn scarcely at all, Jupiter only very slightly and Mars quite conspicuously. No decisive observations of these planets, therefore, could be made; the phases seen favoured Ptolemy as much as Copernicus.

So far as these three planets are concerned, and merely as a matter of geometry, the two rival interpretations of their motions were not so very different. In Figure 5 these planets do 'go round' the sun; in Figure 6 they 'go round' the earth. In fact any one of them will describe a circular path or orbit with the sun as centre if the proportions of Figure 5 are suitably adjusted. Figure 9 illustrates this. The adjustment required is to make the supposed orbit of the sun (S) round the earth (E) the same diameter as the small circle followed by the planet (P) round the steadily-moving centre (C). If this is done, it is easy to see that the length of the line S–P will always be the same – in other words P describes a circle with S as centre. Ptolemy's system would allow of such an adjustment because the diameters of the various circles were entirely arbitrary; all that was necessary was that the small circle (the one on which P stands in Figure 9) should be in the right proportion to the larger circle on which C travels, to fit the observations.

It is interesting to reflect that if Ptolemy had assumed that the small circles of all three outer (or 'superior') planets had the same diameter, equal to the diameter of the sun's supposed orbit round the earth, then the diameters of the three large circles would have had definite values, relative to that of the sun's orbit – and these values would have been correct!

The system proposed by Copernicus was altogether more satisfactory in this respect because the periodic retrograde motions of the superior planets were accounted for as being due *solely* to the earth's revolution round the sun, no other assumption being required. Moreover (as will be explained later) this system enabled the *relative* diameters of all the plane-

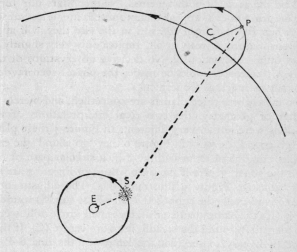

FIGURE 9

tary orbits to be calculated – again, in the case of the superior planets, without making any additional assumption such as that mentioned in the preceding paragraph.

To sum up, Galileo's observations proved that the planets were bodies of the same nature as the earth, and that Venus revolved round the sun. Although formal proof was lacking that the remaining planets (including the earth) revolved round the sun, a wide breach had been made in the Ptolemaic position and the idea that the sun was the centre of motion of the earth and the superior planets, as well as of the two inferior planets, was made immeasurably more probable. This idea had the great merit of simplicity — it accounted for the observed motions without the aid of arbitrary, *ad hoc* assumptions such as Ptolemy had found necessary — and this 'economy of hypothesis' always makes a powerful appeal to the mind.

When the first really accurate observations of the motions of the planets had been made (by the Danish astronomer Tycho Brahe) the time was ripe for a further big advance. This was made by Kepler, who used Tycho Brahe's observations to prove that the paths of the planets round the sun are ellipses and not circles, that the sun is in each case at one of the two foci of the ellipse, that the variations of velocity of a planet along its orbit obey a simple numerical law and that there is a simple numerical relation between the periodic times (the time for one complete revolution of each planet) and the mean distances between the planets and the sun. These facts are merely mentioned here, without further explanation, as they are not strictly relevant to our theme; but it will be evident that it would be entirely beyond the capacity of the Ptolemaic system to account for them, however many further arbitrary assumptions were made.

Newton supplied the final death-blow to the geocentric hypothesis by proving that all the motions of all the bodies comprising the solar system according to Copernicus and Kepler could be accounted for on the one dramatically simple assumption that any particle of matter in the universe attracts any other particle with a force which is directly proportional to the product of their masses and inversely proportional to the square of the distance between them. So far as the geocentric idea is concerned, the still more simple and fundamental theory of Einstein has had no further effect; the idea was dead long before Einstein was born.

To return to our primitive observer, he would have seen other things in the sky besides sun, moon, stars and planets. He would have seen an occasional comet and many 'shooting' or 'falling' stars — meteors, as they are called by astronomers.

We, however, are not concerned with them. He would not have failed to notice the Milky Way, encircling the sky and glowing with faint, inexplicable light, which the first telescope showed to be due to myriads of faint stars. He might have noticed, not far from its margin, an object like a little oval patch of mist; but he could have had no inkling of its tremendous significance.

CHAPTER II

DRAWING THE SOLAR SYSTEM TO SCALE

MANY people say that the sun looks to them about as big as a dinner plate, or a penny, or some other round object. They will tell you that two bright stars, or two planets, that had attracted their attention the previous evening, were about five feet, or five yards, or five inches, apart. Such statements appear to have some definite meaning to those who make them, but as a means of communicating information to others they are valueless. It is useless to refer distances between objects in the sky to a foot-rule or yard-stick *without specifying how far away from the eye the foot-rule or yard-stick is held.*

If anyone doubts this, let him hold a foot-rule at arm's length and 'measure' the distance in inches between two remote objects – trees, chimney-pots, stars, or anything whatever. Suppose the distance is ten inches. Now let him crook his elbow, bringing the foot-rule nearer to the eye. He will find that the distance between the two objects is smaller – eight inches, five inches or some other figure depending on how much the elbow has been crooked.

The sun (or the full moon, which is almost exactly the same apparent size as the sun) can be covered completely by an ordinary pea held at arm's length – a fact which surprises most people, but which can easily be verified by anyone who possesses a pea. A penny just covers the sun or moon when held at a distance of twelve feet. An average dinner-plate would have to be about a hundred and twenty feet away to match sun or moon in apparent size.

Feet, inches, centimetres and other units of *linear* measure are therefore useless for such purposes. *Angular* measure is used instead because it has the same meaning for everybody. Imagine the whole sweep of the horizon to be divided into 360 equal parts. Each part is called a degree. A degree is divided into sixty equal parts called minutes. A minute is itself divided into sixty equal parts called seconds. An angular distance such as three degrees sixteen minutes and forty seconds is written 3° 16' 40" – and it is unfortunate that the little 'o' should also be used for degrees of temperature, the single dash for feet and the double dash for inches. Throughout this book the single and double dashes will always mean minutes and seconds. It is also most unfortunate that these two words are used to designate intervals of time. When speaking, it is customary to avoid confusion by referring to the angular units as 'minutes of arc' and 'seconds of arc', and to the time units as 'minutes (or seconds) of time'.

One further explanation is necessary before we can proceed. The horizon was mentioned in the opening part of the preceding paragraph, but the statements in that paragraph apply to any great circle in the sky. What then is a great circle? Look at a globe of the earth (or a picture of one) and note the parallels of latitude running round the globe in the east-west direction. The equator is one of them. It is unique not only because it is midway between the two poles but also because it is the largest of them. It is a great circle; all the other parallels of latitude are small circles. The meridians of longitude, extending from pole to pole like the divisions between the sections of an orange, are all great circles. Incidentally, if longitude on the earth is measured in degrees along the parallels of latitude (as is the custom) we have the anomaly that two places on the equator, a degree apart, are further apart than two places a degree apart on any other parallel of latitude. This looks rather like a riddle, but a glance at the terrestrial globe will show that it is true.

On the earth, the position of a point is defined by its latitude and longitude, both expressed in degrees, minutes and seconds of arc. In the sky, the equivalent of latitude is called *declination*, and the equivalent of longitude is called *right ascension*. Declination is the angular distance (north or south) of a star or other object from the equator, and is expressed in degrees, minutes and seconds of arc. Right ascension, however, is expressed in hours, minutes and seconds of *time*, thus avoiding the absurdity of units of arc varying in value in different parts of the sky.

When it is stated that the moon's angular diameter at a particular moment is 30', this means only one thing – namely that it would require 720 such moons side by side to fill the whole circumference of a great circle in the sky – any great circle. When it is stated that two stars are 30' apart, this means

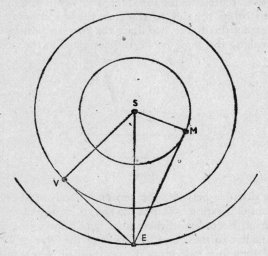

FIGURE 10

that the angular distance between them could just be 'stepped' 720 times round the great circle on which they happen to lie. There is therefore no ambiguity about angular measure as applied to apparent distances in the sky.

Now we are ready to consider the solar system. We know that Mercury and Venus revolve round the sun in orbits lying within the orbit of the earth, and that in consequence the angular distance between the sun and either of these planets is always smaller than 90°. Both planets, in fact, move steadily across the sky away from the sun, either to the east or to the west, slow down, stop, and then move in the reverse direction towards the sun. The moment when either planet is furthest from the sun is known as its maximum elongation; and we will first assume, for the sake of simplicity, that the angular distances at maximum elongation are always the same, as they would be if all three orbits were circular with the sun at the centre.

Figure 10 represents the sun, Mercury, Venus and the earth and their orbits roughly to scale, on the above assumption. To construct this figure, we draw the two lines from E, the earth, making the angle between them equal to the observed

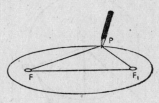

FIGURE 11

angular distance between the sun and Venus at the latter's maximum elongation. We put the sun, S, at any distance we please from E on one of these lines, and draw a line from S perpendicular to the other line, cutting that line at V. This point V therefore represents the position of Venus at maximum elongation, for Euclid (and common sense) tells us that the line EV will be a tangent to a circle with centre at S and radius equal to SV. In other words no part of the circle will be to the left of the line through V, and consequently Venus never appears further from S, as seen from E, than it does when at this point V.

Now we can measure ES and VS, and we have the ratio of the distances of the earth and of Venus from the sun.

The procedure is exactly the same for Mercury, which is shown at M in the figure.

But Kepler showed that these three orbits are ellipses, not circles. Figure 11 shows how to draw an ellipse. A piece of stout, unstretchable thread is looped round two drawing-pins F, F_1 and drawn tight by a pencil P. The pencil is moved round on the paper, keeping the thread taut, and will trace an oval curve as shown. The thread remains the same length throughout the operation, and the sum of the two distances FP and F_1P is therefore constant. An ellipse, in fact, is defined as a curve, the sum of the distances of any point on which from two points is constant. This statement by itself is rather arid, but the drawing pins, the thread and the pencil bring it to life and make its meaning clear. The two points F, F_1 are called the foci (plural of focus) and in all the elliptical planetary orbits the sun is at one of the two foci.

The sum of the two distances FP, F_1P is constant, but the distance FP by itself varies as P moves round the curve. We can make the ellipse fatter or thinner as we please, by varying the distance between the drawing-pins while keeping the length of the thread constant. If we could make the two drawing-pins coincide, the ellipse would become a circle, and FP would always be equal to F_1P. If we moved the pins so far apart as to make the thread nearly taut, and if the thread were really unstretchable, the pencil would trace a very narrow ellipse, in which FP becomes very small (and F_1P very large) at one end, and F_1P very small (and FP very large) at the other.

The orbits of all the planets are all very nearly circular, and their distances from the sun do not vary very much. The most direct way (though not the best way) to determine the shape of the earth's orbit is to measure the angular diameter of the sun at various times of the year. We find that this diameter is greatest on January 4 (32′ 35″) and smallest on July 6 (31′ 32″) so that unquestionably we are nearest to the sun on January 4 and furthest away on July 6. If we draw the distances thus determined on any convenient scale, we have the shape of the earth's orbit.

Now the successive maximum elongations of Venus (and the same applies to Mercury) occur at times when the earth is at various points in its orbit; and of course observation tells us exactly where the earth is at each of these events. As we should expect, the angular distances actually measured at various maximum elongations are not the same. To construct the true orbit of Venus or Mercury, therefore, a much more elaborate diagram than Figure 10 would be required. First we should have to draw the whole elliptical orbit of the earth, determined by measurements of the angular diameter of the sun as explained above, or by one of a number of other methods. Then we should have to follow the instructions given above for constructing Figure 10 for a number of maximum elongations, putting E on each occasion in its proper place in its orbit. In this way the true elliptical orbit of the planet could be drawn, point by point.

Actually, if we are certain beforehand that the orbit is an ellipse (and since Newton's time we *can* be certain) it is necessary only to determine three positions of the planet in our diagram; an ellipse is defined completely if the position of a focus, and of three points on the ellipse itself, are known.

By this method we should discover that the planet does not move always at the same speed in its orbit; when it is nearest to the sun (at perihelion, as it is called) it is moving fastest, and when furthest away (at aphelion) it is moving most slowly.

The same applies to the earth. It is moving faster in January than it is in July, and when constructing the more elaborate form of Figure 10 necessary to determine the orbit of Venus or Mercury, we must take account of the fact in fixing the various positions of the point E.

The procedure for a superior planet is not quite so simple. Figure 12 represents the sun S, the earth E and the planet P in their orbits, supposed to be circular to simplify matters. If the planet would only stand still at the point P there would be no difficulty; we could observe its position among the stars when the earth is at E, and then again when the earth is at E_1. We know the two positions of the two points E, E_1 from the time interval between the observations, we know the angle EPE_1, because that is the angular distance that the planet would have traversed in the sky in that interval, and therefore we can draw the lines EP, E₁P which, intersecting at P, give us the position of the planet.

In Figure 12 the two points E, E₁ have not been chosen arbitrarily; they are the two points at which the sun and the (fictitious) planet would be 90° apart in the sky – the planet would be in quadrature, as the astronomers say. This has been

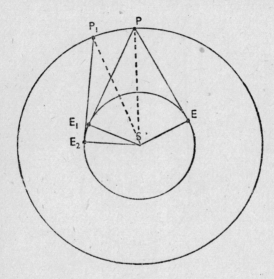

FIGURE 12

done to show the connection between this problem and that of Figure 8, for it will be clear that an observer on the planet P would choose one or other of these moments to observe the earth, because to him the earth would then be at greatest elongation. Another purpose is to show that it is not really necessary to bring in the stars at all; the observations could be confined entirely to the members of the solar system.

The planet, however, does not stay at P; while the earth

has been moving from E to E_1, the planet has moved to P'_1. Our second observation, therefore, will be made from E_2 if we prefer to leave the stars out of consideration and merely note the time of quadrature. This complicates matters, but only slightly. We know the period of revolution of the planet, and therefore we know the fraction of that period that has elapsed between the observation at E and the observation at E_2. In other words, we know the angle PSP_1.

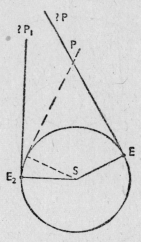

FIGURE 13

To avoid confusion we will begin a new diagram, Figure 13. We do not yet know where the point P is, except that it is somewhere on the line E?P, and similarly all we know about P_1 is that it is somewhere on the line E?P_1. All we have to do is to swing the line SE_2 back through an angle equal to the angle PSP_1 (Figure 12), carrying with it the line E_2P_1 perpendicular to it, as shown in dotted lines. We have now our original diagram, Figure 12, and we know that P was where the dotted line intersects the line E?P when the earth was at E.

Now it has to be explained that astronomers do not actually

proceed in this way; they solve such problems by computation, not by drawing diagrams and measuring them. They would consult tables of trigonometrical functions and obtain the results directly from them. Not everyone, however, has the advantage of a knowledge of trigonometry, and it is the primary purpose of this book to demonstrate the principles underlying the work of astronomers in a way that can be understood by anyone. Those readers who are familiar with mathematics are asked to remember that arguments such as have been used in connection with Figures 10, 12 and 13 are more fundamental than the tables of trigonometrical functions and other specialised tools of the trade, which indeed are based on and derived from the universally understood geometrical or graphical method. Newton, who was no mean mathematician, did not disdain to use this method, and his example is at least as good as any other.

The superior planets, like the inferior planets, revolve in elliptical orbits, and the simplified procedure explained with reference to Figures 12 and 13 is not adequate. It has to be extended in the way described with reference to Figure 10. The determination of three points on the orbit of each planet enables the whole orbit to be drawn or computed, because we know that it is elliptical and that the sun is at a focus of the ellipse.

For the sake of completeness, it must be pointed out that not only does the sun attract the planets, but the planets attract one another. The orbits of all of them are therefore slightly distorted from the true elliptical form, and the speeds with which they move in their orbits are varied from the simple law stated by Kepler. These effects are known as perturbations.

It must also be stated that more planets have been discovered since Galileo's time, and many more moons or satellites circling round the planets. A whole host of very small planets (called asteroids or minor planets) has been discovered between Mars and Jupiter. Uranus, beyond Saturn, was discovered (by accident) by William Herschel in 1781. In 1846 Neptune, beyond Uranus, was discovered by computation on the basis of unpredicted and unexpected variations in the motion of Uranus which could not be explained as perturbations by the planets already known. In 1930 Tombaugh discovered Pluto, beyond Neptune, by detecting its image on a photographic plate. These three extra-Saturnian planets could not have been known before the invention of the telescope because they are too faint to be seen with the naked eye. This is not strictly true of Uranus, which can just be seen with the naked eye; but it could never have been recognised as a planet without a telescope.

It is perhaps of some topical interest that the element Uranium (the raw material of the atomic bomb) was discovered in the same year that Herschel discovered Uranus, and received its name in honour of the new planet. The atomic number of Uranium is 92, and it is the element of highest atomic number in nature. In recent years two new elements, of atomic number 93 and 94, have been produced artificially. They have very aptly been named Neptunium and Plutonium respectively. Beyond Plutonium, other elements of still higher atomic number have been produced, but unfortunately there are no extra-Plutonian planets known to supply them with names. The nuclear physicists have got ahead of the astronomers.

To return to our theme, we are now in a position to draw the solar system to scale or, in mathematical language, to determine the various distances in the solar system in terms of the mean distance between the sun and the earth as unit. In fact this distance is known as the astronomical unit. It is clear that if any one of the various distances can be measured in terrestrial units (miles or kilometres), all the rest of them can be determined at once by calculation, or by measurement of our scale drawing, just as we can determine any distance on a map, or any dimension on an engineer's drawing, when we know the scale.

So far nothing has been said about the distance of the moon from the earth. We will dispose of this now, because it is part of our theme; but, as will be explained, it is a side issue – a blind alley. When we know this distance in miles or kilometres it does not help directly to determine any of the other distances. Indirectly, however, it provides a valuable check, as will be explained.

The distance of the moon is measured by measuring its parallax. For this, as we have already seen, it is necessary to make observations from two different viewpoints. In the case of the planets, the distance between the two view-points was not known in miles or kilometres, but it was known in terms of the astronomical unit – the mean distance between the sun and the earth. When we are dealing with the moon, we find that its parallax is quite large as seen from two different posi-

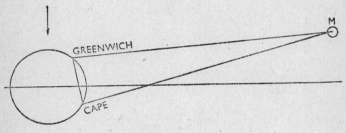

FIGURE 14

tions on the earth, and therefore we can determine its distance directly in miles or kilometres, because we can measure the distance between our two viewpoints in miles or kilometres.

The distance *in a straight line* between the Royal Observatories at Greenwich and at the Cape of Good Hope is about 5400 miles. When the moon is in about 9° north declination it appears from the Cape to be about 1° 18′ further north among the stars than it does from Greenwich. By making a diagram to scale, like Figure 14, or more conveniently and accurately by computation, the distance of the moon from the centre of the earth is found to be about 240,000 miles. This distance is continually varying because not only is the *unperturbed* orbit of the moon round the earth elliptical, not circular, but also this orbit is strongly perturbed by the attraction of the sun, and also slightly by the attraction of the other planets.

The distance can also be determined by a single observer from a single point on the earth. Figure 15 illustrates the method. It is a view of the earth-moon system seen from above the north pole – in the direction of the arrow in Figure 14. We can observe the moon throughout its orbit, measuring its apparent diameter at different times and its position among the stars when it is on the observer's meridian – the great circle passing through the south point on the horizon and through the zenith (the point directly overhead) – and thereby deter-

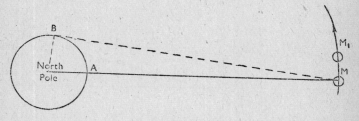

FIGURE 15

mine the shape of its orbit round the *centre* of the earth. But the observer is not at the centre of the earth; he is on the surface and (unless he is at one of the two poles) he is being carried round in a circle by the rotation of the earth about its axis, the diameter of this circle depending on the latitude of his observatory.

In Figure 15 we have imagined the observer to be on the terrestrial equator and the moon to be on the celestial equator. When the observatory is at A the moon is on the meridian; the centre of the earth, the observer, and the centre of the moon are all on the same straight line. As in Figure 12 we first imagined the planet P to be stationary, so in Figure 15 we will first imagine the moon to be stationary. After a little less than six hours the observatory will be at B, 4000 miles or so to one side of the centre of the earth. The (stationary) moon will be setting, but it will not be in the same place among the stars; it will be displaced among them westwards by about 1° roughly. The observer, knowing the radius of the earth in miles, can at once calculate its distance in the way already explained with reference to Figure 14.

In actuality the moon does not stand still; while the observatory is moving from A to B the moon moves from M to M_1; but this can be allowed for, as already explained by reference to Figure 13, and the result is exactly the same. In effect, the moon sets before it should – and of course it also rises later than it should, for the same reason.

This apparent displacement of the moon due to the earth's rotation is known as the moon's horizontal parallax. This does not mean that the displacement is in the horizontal direction – it is not; what is meant is its parallax *on the horizon*. At the equator it varies from about 54′ to about 61′. Taking the radius of the earth to be 3963 miles, these parallaxes correspond to distances varying between about 252,000 miles and 223,000 miles.

It is unfortunate that this distance, so easy to measure, does not give us the *scale* of the solar system. The reason will be clear from a glance at Figure 6. It is clear that the circle representing the orbit of the moon round the earth could be made almost any diameter we please without in any way affecting the proportions of the picture. There is an upper limit to this diameter – it must not be drawn so large as to carry the moon behind any of the planets, because this would be contrary to observed facts. The moon, in its passage across the sky, sometimes comes between us and a planet, hiding it from view – the planet is said to be 'occulted'. This happens to our nearest planetary neighbours, Venus and Mars. Neither is ever seen *in front* of the moon. The moon, therefore, is nearer to us than either of these planets at their nearest.

We must therefore look elsewhere for opportunities of finding the scale of the system. The obvious way would be to measure the parallax of the sun directly, as in the case of the moon, by observing it from two different observatories as far apart as possible. Unfortunately the amount of the parallax is so small that this method would not give a sufficiently accurate result. Whatever method is used, however, it is always converted into the parallax that the centre of the sun would show if observed from two observatories 3963 miles apart – half the diameter of the earth. This quantity is known as the solar parallax. If there could be an observer at the centre of the sun, and if he could see the earth, its angular diameter would to him be twice the solar parallax.

CHAPTER III

FINDING THE SCALE OF
THE SOLAR SYSTEM

THE earliest attempt to determine the solar parallax accurately was made by observing a transit of Venus across the sun. Venus is in line with the earth and the sun twice during its passage from eastern to western elongation and back again. These events are known as 'conjunctions' – Venus is said to be in conjunction with the sun. When it is in conjunction on the far side of the sun the occasion is called superior conjunction; when on the nearer side it is called inferior conjunction.

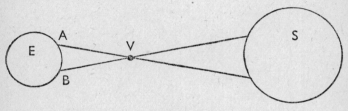

FIGURE 16

If the orbit of Venus were in the same plane as that of the earth, or very nearly so, we should see Venus crossing the disc of the sun at every inferior conjunction; but in actual fact the two orbits are inclined or tilted relative to one another to such an extent that Venus nearly always passes to the north or to the south of the sun. At intervals of 8, 122, 8, 106 and 8 years, however, inferior conjunction occurs when the two planets are near to the parts of the orbits where their planes intersect one another. At these times Venus is seen in transit. The last occasion when this happened was in 1882; the next will be in 2004, then again in 2012.

Figure 16 shows the earth, Venus and the sun, not to scale, the earth and the sun being made much too big for the sake of clearness. When Venus is in transit, it will be seen in the direction AV from observatory A and in the direction BV from observatory B. In other words, it will be seen nearer the northern limb of the sun from B than from A. (Astronomers call the actual edge of the disc of the sun, the moon or a planet the *limb*, to avoid confusion with the terminator of the moon or planet, which could also be called an edge, but is merely the border between the illuminated and unilluminated parts – the sunrise or sunset line.)

Figure 17a shows the sun as seen from observatory A with Venus showing on its surface as a round black spot, the straight line representing its track across the face of the sun. Figure 17b shows the same thing as seen from observatory B, with Venus and its track much further north.

FIGURE 17A   FIGURE 17B

All we have to do, therefore, is to measure the angular distance between the two tracks, and we can then draw a diagram like Figure 16, with the intervals between the earth, Venus and the sun correctly proportioned, and draw the two lines AV and BV making the angle between them equal to the angular distance between the tracks. This last step is the crucial one, because we know the distance between A and B in miles or kilometres, and therefore we have the *scale* of the diagram; we can measure EV and determine its value in miles or kilometres – but in practice, we do it by calculation. Knowing EV, we can find ES, because we know the ratio or proportion between EV and VS – about 2.6.

The transit-of-Venus method was first tried in 1761, and

repeated in 1769 with greater success. It so happened that on both occasions the planet crossed the sun's disc some distance from the centre. If it crosses the sun's disc centrally it takes about eight hours to pass right across. Obviously it crosses in a shorter time if its path is well to the north or south of the centre. More important is the fact that this time (the duration of the transit) will be appreciably different as seen from two places well separated on the earth in the north–south direction. Halley, the second Astronomer Royal, pointed this out nearly a century earlier and suggested that the observers should merely *measure the duration of the transit*, without making any attempt to measure the *position* of the planet on the sun's

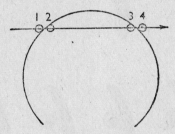

FIGURE 18

disc. The positions of the two tracks could then be deduced from these two durations, their lengths being obviously directly proportional to their durations if we consider only the centre of the planet.

Figure 18 shows Halley's plan. As will be seen, there are four moments when the limb of Venus appears to be in contact with the limb of the sun, these being called the first, second, third and fourth contacts. Obviously first contact cannot be observed accurately because the planet is invisible until a part of it actually encroaches upon the sun to take a 'bite' out of it – and that will be too late; first contact occurred before there was any noticeable 'bite'. Much the same can be said for fourth contact; it is very difficult to be certain when the last little bite has just disappeared. Halley, however, was confident that second and third contacts could be timed accurately; he expected that the planet would look like Figure 19 at these moments.

The observers found, however, that it did not look like that; instead, as the planet entered upon the sun's disc it seemed to draw after it a strip of dark sky, which gradually

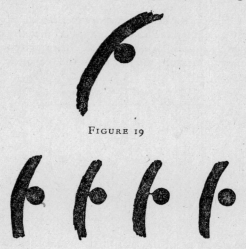

FIGURE 19

FIGURE 20

became narrower and finally disappeared when the planet was well within the limb of the sun – or appeared to be. The same thing happened in reverse as the planet passed off the disc of the sun at the end of the transit. The observers were therefore in doubt as to the exact moments of second and third contacts, and this uncertainty detracted seriously from the accuracy of the result.

This strange effect, which became known as the 'Black Drop', was a mystery to the observers at that time. We know the explanation now – it is a purely optical effect, causing the bright sun to appear larger than it really is and the dark planet to appear smaller than it really is. True contact occurs at the moment when the dark filament disappears (second contact) or appears (third contact), although at those moments the planet appears to be well within the sun's limb. Figure 20 shows four successive stages of this effect at 'ingress' – the beginning of the transit.

In Halley's method the observers had to travel to parts of the earth in high northern and southern latitudes, and success depended upon both of them being able to observe both ingress and egress – the beginning and the end of the transit. They did not need to know their longitude accurately, nor was it necessary for their clocks to show accurate Greenwich time; all they had to do was to run accurately for the few hours of the actual transit. This was just as well, because in those days there were no portable clocks which could be relied on to keep accurate time during the months required for the observers to reach their observing stations. For this very reason, also, longitudes were known only approximately. In the course of the next hundred years or so, however, chronometers were developed which could be depended upon to maintain a nearly constant rate for many months, or even years; and in consequence navigation and the determination of longitude became very much more certain and accurate.

By the time the next pair of transits of Venus occurred, in 1874 and 1882, a different method was available which, although it required accurate knowledge of longitude and accurate knowledge of Greenwich time at the observing stations, had two great advantages; it required observations of only one phase of the transit – ingress only or egress only – and instead of the observers having to take up their stations in bleak sub-arctic and antarctic latitudes, they could be near the equator; and the nearer the better.

This method, proposed by the French astronomer Delisle, is similar in principle to the procedure described with reference to Figure 15 for determining the distance of the moon from a single point on the earth. In Figure 21 two observers

A and B, both on the equator and separated by a wide interval of longitude, are equipped with chronometers showing Greenwich time. They have chosen their positions so that one of them will see the beginning of the transit soon after sunrise, while the other will see it shortly before sunset. They know their longitudes accurately, and therefore, after they have timed second contact as accurately as possible, they will know their exact positions in space in relation to Venus and the sun. The diagram can therefore be drawn accurately to scale, and, since we know the size of the earth, we know the actual scale and can measure all parts of the diagram in miles or kilometres.

Note that in the interval between A's and B's observations Venus has travelled some distance round its orbit. We know,

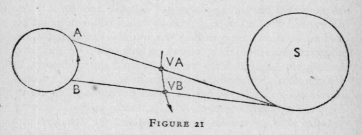

FIGURE 21

however, what proportion of its whole orbit it has traversed in that interval because we know the time (584 days) taken by Venus to travel right round its orbit in relation to the moving earth. We can therefore draw all parts of the diagram to scale. The analogy with Figures 12 and 13 will be noted.

This method was used in 1874 and again in 1882; but the 'black drop' difficulty (and others) again largely vitiated the results, and it was appreciated that observations of transits of Venus could not afford the same accuracy as other methods that had been developed in the meantime. It is very unlikely that astronomers will take any particular interest in the transit of 2004 A.D.

As early as 1680 attempts had been made by French astronomers, observing in France and in South America, to determine the parallax of Mars. By this time the reader will need no detailed explanation of the method used; it will be evident that Mars as seen from France and from South America will appear in slightly different positions among the stars, and that the procedure is essentially the same as in the case of the moon, explained with reference to Figure 14. The parallax of Mars, however, even when nearest to the earth, is only about 1/140 of that of the moon, and it is therefore not surprising that in in the seventeenth century the result was not very accurate. However, the distance of the earth from the sun, derived from these early observations, was creditably near the true value – about ten per cent. too small.

In the second half of the nineteenth century more accurate observations of Mars were made. Instead of observing from two different stations on the earth, it was found better to observe from a single station and to measure the parallax due to the earth's rotation – the method of Figure 15 again. The fact that Mars is a globe of considerable angular diameter, however, made it difficult to measure its angular distance from stars, which appear as mere points of light in the telescope, and for this reason parallax observations were made of some of the minor planets. These have already been mentioned. They are very small bodies, mostly only a few miles in diameter, which revolve round the sun in orbits lying for the most part between Mars and Jupiter. The orbits of the brighter of them are well determined and they are just as much members of the solar family as the major planets. The measurement of the parallax of any one of them will therefore give the scale of the solar system. Those that were observed in the nineteenth century are more distant than Mars, and therefore have a smaller parallax, but this is offset by the fact that, like the stars, they appear as mere points of light in the telescope, and their positions among the stars can therefore be measured more accurately.

The results from the observations of these minor planets were in very good agreement with those derived from observations of Mars, and by the close of the century the value of the solar parallax was known with considerable accuracy.

In 1898 a remarkable minor planet, named Eros, was discovered. It is remarkable in that its mean distance from the sun is less than that of Mars, and that because its orbit is very elliptical it sometimes comes closer to the earth than any other planet – slightly more than half the distance of Venus at her nearest and slightly more than one third the distance of Mars at his nearest.

Measurements of the parallax of Eros during its close approaches to the earth would therefore be expected to be at least three times more certain than those of the parallax of Mars, and also much more certain than those of the minor planets previously used, which do not come so near to us as Mars.

Another very important advance had been made in the meantime – the application of photography to astronomy. The measurement of angular distances in the sky by visual means requires great skill in the observer and the number of measurements that can be made in a given time is limited. They have to be made often in very uncomfortable conditions which militate against accuracy. In the case of transient events, such as the passage of a minor planet across the sky, a mistake on the part of a single observer cannot afterwards be checked or rectified; the only safeguard is to employ two or more observers using similar instruments, but this can rarely be done – skilled observers and the costly instruments that they use are always in short supply. Photography alters the position entirely; no great skill is required to expose the plates, and once they have been developed they constitute a permanent record which can be studied at leisure and in comfort. The distances between the images of stars and minor planet or other object can be measured at any time and by any number of persons, so that accidental errors of measurement can be detected and eliminated. Moreover, the number of star images on the plates is very great and as many of them as desired may be used as reference stars, because there is no restriction on the time that can be spent in measurement.

It is not surprising, therefore, that modern determinations of the solar parallax by photographic observations of Eros are very accurate indeed – far more accurate and reliable than those made by visual means in the nineteenth century. The last such determination was made by Sir Harold Spencer Jones, the present Astronomer Royal. He used observations of Eros made in 1930 and 1931 by no fewer than twenty-four observatories in all parts of the world, including the Cape Observatory (Cape Town) of which he was then the Director in his capacity as His Majesty's Astronomer at the Cape of Good Hope. For this work he was awarded the Gold Medal of the Royal Astronomical Society in 1943.

This latest value of the solar parallax is 8″.790 ± 0″.001. This means that the exact value may be anywhere between 8″.791 and 8″.789. As the earth's equatorial radius (or semi-diameter) is 3963 miles, this implies that the mean distance between the centre of the sun and the centre of the earth lies somewhere between 92,990,000 and 93,000,000 miles. The uncertainty is much less than it was in the best earlier determinations.

Owing to the fact that observations were made at so many different observatories, spread over such a wide area of the earth, it was possible to combine them in several different ways, thereby obtaining a number of different solutions of the problem which checked one another and enhanced the accuracy of the final result. Every care was taken to trace and remove causes of systematic error, and all the observations were scrutinised with critical care. It is very improbable that an improved value of the solar parallax will ever be obtained by observing the parallax of Eros.

At first sight it may seem that an uncertainty of 10,000 miles is unduly large, but it must be remembered that it represents only one part in 9000. This is equivalent to measuring an object 9 inches long with an uncertainty of one thousandth of an inch. Engineers are not often required to measure such objects with much greater accuracy than that.

Before passing on to other subjects, let us dwell upon the extreme smallness of one second of arc. A halfpenny, one inch in diameter, would have an angular diameter of 1″ if viewed from a distance of 206,265 inches, that is, about three and one quarter miles. The total uncertainty of the latest value of the solar parallax (0″.002) corresponds to a halfpenny seen from a distance of 1625 miles – the distance between London and Moscow. A human hair is about one five hundredth of an inch in diameter. It would have to be seen from a distance of slightly more than 34 feet to appear to have an angular width of 1″, or from a distance of three and one quarter miles to appear to have an angular width of 0″.002.

It has now been shown how the various distances within the solar system have been determined (by determining one of them) in terms of distances measured on the earth in terrestrial units of length. The principle employed is *parallax*, which is familiar to all of us in everyday life. It might, however, be urged that we have no rigid proof that this principle is valid at great distances from the earth. We can always check the distances determined by parallax on the earth, by means of a tape measure, but we cannot check astronomical distances that way. Is there any way of checking these distances and satisfying ourselves that parallax is valid at great distances from the earth? Fortunately there are several such checks.

The most interesting from the historical point of view is that based on the eclipses of the satellites of Jupiter. Observations of these eclipses gave the first proof that light travels with finite velocity (it takes time for it to pass from A to B) and also gave the first estimate of its actual velocity. Now, when we know the velocity of light by direct experiment, these same observations give us a reasonably accurate value of the solar parallax.

The four bright satellites of Jupiter revolve round the planet in definite periods which are accurately known. From time to time one or other of them enters the shadow cast by the planet itself, and disappears, to reappear later from the other edge of the shadow. These eclipses can be predicted accurately long in advance – and incidentally they can be observed by means of a pair of ordinary field-glasses. In 1675 Ole Roemer, a Danish astronomer, found that the eclipses did not keep to the predicted times; if he began with the eclipses occurring at the time of opposition of Jupiter (when it is nearest to the earth), the succeeding eclipses occurred later than the calculated times, falling gradually further behind as the planet receded from the earth. Later, when the planet was approaching the next opposition, the eclipses gradually caught up again and were once more on time at opposition. He interpreted this correctly as due to the varying distance that the light from the satellite had to travel to reach the earth. He did not know the solar parallax accurately and he was therefore unable to derive an accurate value for the velocity of light. Moreover, the eclipses of these satellites are not instantaneous (their disappearance or reappearance is a matter of minutes) and Roemer could not time them accurately. Nowadays, however, special methods enable the times of the eclipses to be determined with accuracy.

Predictions of the eclipses and other phenomena of Jupiter's satellites are published in the Nautical Almanac (they were useful at one time in determining longitude) and in the Handbook of the British Astronomical Association. Naturally, in these publications the predicted times are computed with due regard to the varying distance between the earth and Jupiter and the consequent varying time of light-travel.

Now that the velocity of light is known by actual measurement, independently of astronomical events, the argument can be turned the other way round. The velocity of light and the observed variation with distance of the times of the eclipses of these satellites being known, the actual distance can be calculated. The calculation is so simple that anyone can do it. The eclipses are later by 1000 seconds when Jupiter is in conjunction (on the far side of the sun from the earth) than they are when Jupiter is in opposition. This is because the light has had to travel, in the first case, a distance greater than in the second case by the diameter of the earth's orbit. Light travels at 186,000 miles per second. Therefore the diameter of the earth's orbit is 186,000 × 1000 = 186,000,000 miles.

Another check on the parallactic method is provided by what is known as the aberration of light (although strictly it ought to be known as the aberration of the stars) which can easily be understood by recalling what happens on a rainy, windless day when one is travelling in a train. When the train is stationary the rain is seen to descend vertically; but when the train is in motion it appears to the passengers to be descending obliquely, as if coming not from directly overhead but from a point some distance ahead of the zenith.

As the earth travels round the sun light from the stars behaves in the same way. At one particular time the earth is travelling towards a certain point in the sky, while six months later it is travelling directly away from that point. Light from a star directly north or south of the plane of the earth's orbit is travelling at 186,000 miles per second. It will not appear to us to strike the earth exactly in the same direction as it would if it reached us instantaneously – with infinite velocity – and consequently the star will appear displaced slightly from its 'proper' position. Six months later it will appear displaced in the opposite direction, because the earth is now travelling in the reverse direction, and observations show that the double displacement amounts to about 41″. The displacement of the star from its 'proper' position is half of this – 20″.5. The velocity of the earth in its orbit is therefore a small fraction of the velocity of light. This fraction is $\frac{20 \cdot 5}{206265}$. Multiplying this by the velocity of light (186,000 miles per second) we get 18.48 miles per second as the orbital velocity of the earth. As there are 31,577,600 seconds in one year, we obtain the circumference of the orbit by multiplying this by 18.48, obtaining 58,355,404,800 miles (which, however, we will call 58,360,000,000 to avoid absurdity) and this, divided by 2π (6.283), gives the *radius* of the orbit as 92,890,000 miles.

Both these methods are independent of parallax and independent of any distance measured on the earth. The only assumption made is that the velocity of light in outer space is the same as its velocity measured in a vacuum on the earth. This assumption is highly probable, but there is no rigid proof that it is true. It will be agreed that the close agreement between the values of the sun's distance obtained by these purely physical methods with that obtained by parallax measurements enhances the probability (to say the least) that all the assumptions made are valid.

There is still another check, also of a physical character, which will be mentioned in Chapter 5.

It was mentioned earlier that the distance of the moon from the earth provided an indirect method of checking the solar parallax. This is due to the fact that to say that the moon revolves round the earth is only a half-truth. The earth, it is true, is about eighty times as heavy as the moon, but nevertheless the moon exerts an appreciable gravitational effect on the earth, and the result is that both the moon and the earth revolve round a point lying between their centres. If the moon and the earth were of equal mass this point would be midway between them, but as the earth is so much more massive than the moon the point is nearer to the earth than to the moon. In fact it is inside the earth, at about 2900 miles from its centre.

During each lunation, therefore, the centre of the earth describes a circle nearly 5800 miles in diameter about this point, which itself moves steadily round the sun, reminding us of the imaginary circles of the Ptolemaic system (Figure 5). This motion of the earth is 'reflected' in the apparent motions of the planets and it therefore provides in theory a means of determining their distances from us.

Now it has to be admitted that this is not a very satisfactory method because it presupposes a knowledge of the mass of the moon. In practice, the most accurate way of determining this mass is first to measure the solar parallax by some other method, then to deduce from observations of the planets the diameter of the small monthly orbit described by the centre of the earth, and from this to calculate the ratio (quoted above as eighty) between the mass of the earth and the mass of the moon. We are therefore in danger of following a circular argument, leading nowhere. However, there are other ways of determining this ratio, not depending on solar parallax, and they agree with the value determined by using the solar parallax as a starting point. In this way a knowledge of the distance of the moon from the earth helps in checking the results of other methods, though it does not improve the accuracy of the result.

Another method makes use of the fact that the ratio, or proportion, of the mass of the earth to that of the sun, can be found from the perturbations of Mars and Venus by the earth, and when this ratio is known the distance between the earth and the sun can be calculated. In this case the only assumption made is that Newton's law of gravitation is true. Measurements of parallax do not enter into it, nor does the velocity of light. The value of the solar parallax found by this and other 'gravitational' methods is in very close agreement with those based on other assumptions. The probability mentioned in the preceding paragraph is therefore still further enhanced. Those readers who have followed the argument so far will find it difficult to entertain any reasonable doubt that parallax operates throughout the solar system as it does on the earth, that the velocity of light is the same in outer space as it is in the laboratory, that Newton's law of gravitation is valid and that the mean distance between the centres of the earth and the sun is about 93,000,000 miles.

The proportions of the solar system can be visualised by contemplating a scale model, due to Sir John Herschel. In this model the sun is represented by a ball 2 feet in diameter. Mercury is a grain of mustard seed 164 feet away from the centre of the ball, Venus is a pea 284 feet away, the earth also a pea 430 feet away, Mars a large pin's head 654 feet away, the asteroids, tiny grains of sand and dust between 1000 and 1200 feet, Jupiter, a good-sized orange nearly a quarter of a mile away, Saturn a small orange at two-fifths of a mile, Uranus a small plum at three-quarters of a mile and Neptune a good sized plum at a mile and a quarter – to which we now have to add Pluto, a small pea at three and a quarter miles.

CHAPTER IV

THE DISTANCES OF THE STARS

By the time the Copernican or heliocentric conception of the solar system had been generally accepted it had to be admitted that the stars were very remote indeed because the wide sweep executed by the earth each year did not change their relative positions in the slightest, nor their spacing in the sky – so far as could be judged by the crude instrumental means available at the time. When it became clear that the distance of the earth from the sun was at least ten thousand times the diameter of the earth it was felt that a movement of twice this enormous distance should produce a parallactic movement of some stars at least that could be detected by appropriate refined methods. Yet it was not until 1838 that success was achieved. Earlier unsuccessful attempts, however, led to two very important accidental discoveries.

The first of these was the discovery by James Bradley of the aberration of the fixed stars, explained in the previous chapter as an effect of the finite velocity of light and the orbital movement of the earth. In 1725 Bradley, the third Astronomer Royal, set up a telescope in a rigidly fixed position such that a star which passed nearly directly overhead (γ Draconis) would come into view in the telescope as it crossed the meridian night by night. He found that it changed its position throughout the year, being farthest south in March and farthest north in September. His method of observation was not capable of showing any displacement east or west. The full extent of the north–south displacement was about 40″. He was puzzled because if this were a *parallactic* displacement the star should have been farthest south in December and farthest north in June.

Various explanations suggested themselves to him, but were rejected after further observations had shown that they were not in accordance with the facts. Another telescope was set up and arranged so that several different stars could be observed. In 1728 the correct explanation occurred to him – the explanation already given in Chapter 3, where the analogy afforded by falling rain was mentioned. It is not known for certain what led Bradley to think of the correct explanation; it may have been the rain. There is a story (not supported by very strong evidence) that he was led to it while sailing on the Thames. According to this story he noticed that the direction in which the pennant at the masthead pointed changed when the boat tacked – for example it might be pointing east when on the starboard tack and north when on the port tack (although he would have called it the larboard tack). He saw that this was due to the forward movement of the boat, first in one direction and then in the other, combining with the constant direction of the wind. Substitute the earth for the boat, his telescope for the pennant and light for the wind, and the analogy is complete.

Having by now observed several stars throughout the year, Bradley found that this explanation fitted all the observations, and since his time every star in the sky has been found to be affected by aberration, precisely in accordance with its position in relation to the earth's orbit. Those in the plane of this orbit appear to move backwards and forwards in a straight line, those in directions at right angles to this plane appear to move in circular paths, and those in intermediate positions appear to move in elliptical paths.

Bradley's discovery was very important indeed; it provided convincing direct evidence that the earth did in fact move as Copernicus had taught and that light had a finite velocity as Roemer had maintained, it provided a means of determining either velocity when the other was known and it afforded a means of determining the solar parallax; but it did not tell us the distance of γ Draconis or of any other star.

William Herschel, the discoverer of Uranus, tried to detect parallactic displacement of stars by studying pairs of stars which are very close together. Many stars which appear single to the naked eye are actually double, and this was one of the many facts disclosed by the telescope. Castor, one of the 'twins', is the best known example of a double star.

Herschel assumed that the closeness of the two components of such a double star was merely apparent – that in some cases at least one of the stars would be very much further away than the other, the two appearing close together to us merely because they are nearly in the same line of sight. If this were so, he could reasonably hope to find a parallactic displacement of one of them relative to the other as the earth revolved round the sun – closer together in March, for example, than in September. He found instead that in many cases the two stars were revolving round one another, just as the earth and the moon revolve round one another, but very much more slowly. He began these observations some time before 1782; in 1803 he announced that the line joining the two components of Castor changed its direction progressively at such a rate as to complete one revolution in about 340 years. He also announced that he had found five other double stars which did the same; but he did not find any alternating change of angular distance with a period of one year, such as might have been observed if his original assumption had been correct.

Like Bradley, Herschel failed to detect stellar parallax but discovered something quite different instead – the first step in the proof that gravitation, the agency operating among the members of the solar system to maintain them in their orbits, also operates among the stars.

Herschel's scheme was perfectly sound in principle, but he did not appreciate how extremely improbable it is that any two conspicuous stars, differing greatly in distance from the earth, would appear only a few seconds of arc apart. He chose, in fact, the only objects in the sky which were practically certain not to show any relative parallax.

At first sight it may seem odd, in view of this last statement, that the first two stars to have their distances measured were double stars – a star in the constellation of the Swan called 61 Cygni and a bright star, invisible from Britain because it is too far south, called α Centauri – the brightest star in the constellation Centaurus. (On the Australian flag there are five stars – four forming the Southern Cross and a fifth some distance away. This fifth star is β Centauri. α Centauri is about 5° nearly due east of β – that is, α and β are about as far apart as the well-known 'pointers' in the Great Bear, known also as the Plough, or the Big Dipper). The observers, however, did not measure the angular distance between the two components – they knew that it would be useless to do so.

Why then were these stars chosen? It is obviously a waste of time to measure the angular distance between two stars with the object of detecting parallax unless there is some reasonable probability that one of them is much nearer than the other. Astronomers therefore consider very carefully any clues that there may be leading to a suspicion that a star is nearer than the average. We can assume that on the average bright stars are nearer than faint stars, but this would not justify us in thinking that any particular bright star is close to us; it might be a very large star a long way away. The only clue available in the early nineteenth century was the speed at which a star moved across the sky. The reader may be surprised to learn that stars move across the sky, particularly as they are sometimes referred to as the *fixed* stars (to distinguish them from the planets), but it is a fact that they are all in motion among themselves. The sun is no exception – it has its own motion relative to the surrounding stars, carrying all the planets with it, in a straight line at a speed of about twelve miles per second. This motion is 'reflected' in the apparent motion of the nearer stars; just as the lamp-posts, houses and other objects at the roadside appear to move backwards as we travel along the road, the nearer stars at the sides of the sun's track appear to move past us backwards, those 'in front' of us appear to spread apart and those 'behind' appear to close in. These 'reflected' movements are superimposed on the 'real' motions of the stars themselves. In some cases the 'reflected' motion may more or less cancel the 'real' motion, but if a star has an unusually rapid motion it is fairly safe to assume that it is near to us, whether the motion is wholly 'reflected' or partly 'reflected' and partly 'real'.

These motions are all exceedingly small in amount – as is obvious, otherwise the constellations would change their shape in course of time, and they have not changed appreciably for centuries. 61 Cygni moves across the sky at an angular speed of 5″ per year – an unusually high speed. It would take only 360 years to move through an angular distance equal to the apparent diameter of the moon. The vast majority of the stars which move at all have motions measured in seconds of arc per century.

These motions of the stars across the sky are called 'proper motion', the word 'proper' being used in its original sense of 'own', or 'belonging to'.

Friedrich Wilhelm Bessel, Prussian State Astronomer, observing at Königsberg, selected 61 Cygni on account of its large proper motion, not because it is a double star – that was fortuitous. He measured the angular distances between this star and two neighbouring faint stars, which had no appreciable proper motion, at intervals throughout the year, and found that its apparent motion relative to these two stars was a wavy line, and that the line swung one way at one time of the year and the other way six months later. The amount of the 'swing' on each side was about one-third of a second of arc.

This result was announced in 1838. Two years later, as a result of further observations, Bessel was able to say that his first result was confirmed. This then was the first successful measurement of the parallax of a star. Bessel's value of the parallax of 61 Cygni has been confirmed by later observations – a remarkable tribute to his ability as an observer.

Thomas Henderson, His Majesty's Astronomer at the Cape, selected α Centauri because it has a proper motion of nearly 4″ per annum. This star also happened to be a double star, but that is not why it was selected. He found, in 1839, by the same method that Bessel had used, that its parallax was nearly one second of arc, although later measurements have reduced this value to o″.76.

In 1840 Friedrich Georg Wilhelm Struve, observing at Pulkovo near St. Petersburg (now Leningrad) obtained a parallax of one-quarter of a second of arc for α Lyrae, the well-known star Vega: but this has since been found to be an over-estimate – it is more nearly one-tenth of a second.

Thus within the space of two years this enormous step forward had been taken simultaneously and independently in three different countries by three different observers. It was not long before other stars were added to the list and at last it was possible to begin to visualise the scale of the stellar system. In the scale model referred to at the end of Chapter 3, α Centauri would have to be placed about 24,000 miles from the two-foot ball representing the sun. 61 Cygni would be 60,000 miles away.

It has been said already that one inch seen at a distance of 206,265 inches has an angular width of 1″. The same applies to one foot at a distance of 206,265 feet, and to one astronomical unit (the mean distance between the earth and the sun) at a distance of 206,265 astronomical units. A star having a parallax of 1″ (if there were such a star) would therefore be 206,265 ×93,000,000 miles from us. α Centauri, with a parallax of 0″.76, is 206,265 ×93,000,000÷0.76 miles away. The distance of 61 Cygni is 206,265 ×93,000,000÷0.30 miles, and so on.

There is really not much point in doing these multiplication sums; we are not concerned with miles in the stellar universe. A much larger unit is used, namely the distance of an object having a parallax of 1″. This unit is appropriately called a parsec. It will be apparent at once that the distance of α Centauri in parsecs is 1÷0.76, or 1.32, that of 61 Cygni is 3.3, and so on. The distance of a star in parsecs is the *reciprocal* of its parallax.

Another unit sometimes employed, especially in popular literature, is the light-year – the distance traversed by light in one year. A little arithmetic, with numbers already given, shows that a parsec is equal to 3.26 light-years. α Centauri is 3.26 × 1.32 = 4.30 light-years away. The distance of 61 Cygni is 3.26 × 3.3 = 10.8 light-years.

The introduction of photographic methods made it possible to extend parallax measurements to greater numbers of stars and greatly improved their accuracy. The parallax method, however, has serious limitations. In the first place, the parallax is extremely small even in the case of the nearest stars. There is a faint star, appropriately named Proxima Centauri, not far from α Centauri in the sky, which has a parallax of 0″.79. It is the nearest known star, α Centauri being slightly further away (parallax 0″.76). A halfpenny would have to be placed 261,100 inches away (a little more than four miles) to have an angular diameter of 0″.79. Only a few stars are known with parallaxes larger than 0″.1 (that is, nearer than 10 parsecs or 32.6 light-years). As the distances increase and the parallaxes become smaller the relative uncertainty increases. Direct, measured parallaxes smaller than 0″.01 (100 parsecs) are very uncertain indeed.

This uncertainty is increased by the fact that we have no knowledge of the distances of the reference stars – they are simply assumed to be so remote as to have no appreciable parallax. Sometimes the parallax turns out to be *negative* – that is to say, the star apparently shifts in the *same* direction as the earth moves, instead of in the opposite direction. A moment's thought will show that there is nothing mysterious about this – it merely means that we have guessed wrong, and that one or more of the reference stars is nearer to us than the star whose parallax we are trying to measure. What the astronomer does is to find out which of the reference stars is to blame, and to put it on the list for measurement.

It sometimes happens to us that we are uncertain which of two distant objects, nearly in the same line of sight, is nearer to us. We move sideways a little – to the right, for example. If the objects move apart, we know that the right-hand object is further away than the other; if they move towards one another the left-hand object is more distant. We do this almost without thinking – certainly without thinking of such words as 'parallax', let alone 'negative parallax'. The principle is exactly the same in the case of the stars.

In theory it is possible to do without reference stars; the positions of stars can be measured by reference to fixed objects on the earth – the divided circles (things like very large, extremely accurate protractors) of suitably mounted telescopes. Indeed this has been done in the case of stars having relatively large parallaxes; but the practical difficulties are very great, the accuracy is not high and the 'output' is small. It takes a very long time to make the necessary measurements, and many more stars can be dealt with in a given time by taking photographs, which can be measured at leisure.

Something may now be said about the instruments employed in these investigations. A telescope is a very simple instrument indeed. It is a long tube with a large lens (called the object-glass) at one end and a tiny lens (called the eye-piece) at the other. The large lens forms an image of distant objects at the other end of the tube, just as the lens of a camera forms an image on the film, plate or focussing screen, and just as the front part of the eye forms an image on the retina at the back of the eye. In the case of a camera, the image is still there even when there is no film in the camera – so long as the shutter is open, of course. In these days of miniature film cameras the 'stand' camera with ground glass focussing screen is not the familiar object that it was, but it is still used by professional portrait photographers. The image or picture is visible, upside down, on the ground glass and the photographer sometimes looks at it through a magnifying glass to make sure that the camera is focussed properly. If, while he is doing this, someone were to remove the focussing screen, the camera would immediately become a telescope – and an astronomical telescope at that; the photographer would still see the image, enlarged by the magnifying glass, and looking very much clearer and brighter than before.

The image being upside down, telescopes for terrestrial use have to be provided with devices for turning it right way up – 'erecting' it, as the opticians say. The long collapsible telescopes such as sailors use have two additional lenses for this purpose – and the instrument is much lengthened thereby.

Field glasses have prisms to erect the image – hence the name 'prismatic binoculars' – and these prisms greatly shorten the instrument.

A telescope having only a lens to form the image and a magnifier to enable this image to be seen enlarged is classed as an astronomical telescope because it is no use for terrestrial purposes. The astronomer does not mind seeing the image upside down, because there is neither up nor down in the sky; but he would mind the loss of light and impairment of definition that would be caused by any erecting device.

In passing, we may mention that the telescope made and used by Galileo was of a different type the only merit of which was that the image was right way up. Ordinary opera-glasses consist of two such telescopes fixed together side by side. They are sometimes called in consequence 'Galilean binoculars' – not because they are made in Palestine. Unscrupulous makers have been known to provide such binoculars with large projections at the sides, to make the unwary think that they are prism binoculars. They can easily be distinguished by the fact that the eyepieces are in line with the object-glasses; in prism binoculars the object-glasses are always further apart than the eyepieces.

However, we are straying from our subject. To return to the portrait camera, when the image is properly in focus on the ground glass screen the photographer of course sees the image and the granular surface of the screen equally sharply – they are in the same plane. If he moves his eye sideways he will see no displacement of one relative to the other. If, instead of a ground glass screen, a fine wire were to be placed across the back of the camera, in the exact position previously occupied by the surface of the screen, the observer would see this wire superimposed on the image and, if it is exactly in register with some particular point of the image, it will remain in register with it even if the eye is moved a little sideways.

All this may seem very obvious, but its importance was not recognised until about forty years after the invention of the telescope. The importance consists in the fact that a telescope having a very fine wire, or two wires crossing one another, in the plane of the image (the focal plane as it is called) is an immensely accurate *pointer*. Before this was recognised, observers had used devices similar to rifle sights for pointing at stars and other objects to determine their position in the sky. In using such a device, as every rifleman knows, it is necessary to keep the object aimed at, the foresight, the backsight and the eye – four separate things – in accurate alignment. The first three are all at different distances from the eye and therefore cannot be seen sharply simultaneously. The object is not enlarged – and the wonder is that anyone ever hits the target with an ordinary rifle, or that Tycho Brahe and his contemporaries could make observations (as they certainly did) that were of any value at all.

Now consider a telescope with cross-wires in its focal plane. All we have to do is to move the telescope about until the crossing point of the two wires coincides with the point in the image that we are aiming at. Both are in sharp focus, the eye need not be centred very accurately at the eyepiece, it does not matter if the head wobbles a trifle, and above all the image is enlarged. Short-sighted people are on an equality with those having normal vision because they need only move the eyepiece a trifle to bring the image and the wires into sharp focus. The increase in accuracy is enormous.

This discovery was made by an Englishman, William Gascoigne, who was killed at an early age at the battle of Marston Moor in 1644. The discovery did not become widely known, and it was not until twenty-two years after Gascoigne's death that Auzout, a Frenchman, hit upon it again – which serves to show that the obvious is sometimes hard to see.

The time that this device came into general use was an epoch; it was the beginning of the modern period of accurate astronomical observation of position.

Gascoigne (and later Auzout) also pointed out that an extension of this principle provided a means of measuring accurately small angular distances. All that is necessary is to provide *two* wires, parallel to one another, one of which is movable towards and away from the other by means of an accurately made screw. The telescope is adjusted so that the fixed wire is coincident with one star (or other object) and the screw is rotated until the movable wire is coincident with the other star or object. The number of turns of the screw, and the fraction of a turn, give the distance between the two images, and this is easily converted into angular distance in the sky. A third wire, perpendicular to the other two, is necessary – and all three wires are mounted in a casing which can be rotated to bring the third wire (the 'position' wire) into coincidence with both objects. This casing is provided with a divided circle (an accurate protractor) so that the angular *position* (always referred to as the position-angle) of the line adjoining the two

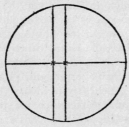

FIGURE 22

objects can be determined. The appearance of the field of view of a telescope fitted with this device is shown in Figure 22, with the wires set upon two stars. The device is known as the filar micrometer (from Latin 'filum', a thread) and for over two centuries, until very recently, it had no real rival for the measurement of angular distances less than one second of arc.

The 'wires' are actually very fine spider-webs – a statement which laymen often find hard to believe; but it is true – nothing else will serve the purpose.

Bessel and Henderson used a different type of instrument, called a heliometer, which was devised originally for measuring the angular diameter of the sun (Greek – helios, the sun; metron, a measure). It was rather better than the filar micrometer at measuring angular distances of one minute of arc and upwards, and was capable of high precision in the hands of a highly skilled observer. It has now gone out of use, and for that reason will not be further described.

Having explained how a camera can be turned into a telescope, we now ask the reader to turn the telescope back into a camera by removing the eyepiece, the micrometer and everything which has to do with *visual* observing, and substituting a plate-holder. That is the instrument used nowadays for measurement of proper motions, stellar parallax, positions of minor planets and comets and a host of other tasks formerly done by eye. Nearly everything in astronomy can be done better by photography than by eye. The most important exceptions are the measurement of close double stars, the scrutiny of the surface markings on planets and the study of meteors, for which last no telescope is required at all.

An astronomical camera, or photographic telescope, although essentially the same as any other camera, is very different in its proportions. A typical camera for ordinary use has a lens of about 1 inch aperture and $4\frac{1}{2}$ inches focal length and a plate or film $3\frac{1}{4}$ inches by $2\frac{1}{4}$ inches. The telescope used at the Royal Observatory, Greenwich, for stellar parallax work has a lens, or object-glass, of 26 inches aperture and 22 feet 5 inches focal length, while the plate is only 6 inches square. The images of two stars 1″ apart in the sky are 0.0013 inch apart on the plate – just over one thousandth of an inch.

Both in exposing the plates and in measuring them after development the most elaborate precautions are taken to guard against systematic errors. If the 'parallax' star is much brighter than the reference stars, as is often the case, a device (called an occulting shutter) is used to shut off its light periodically so that its image on the plate is no denser and no larger than those of the reference stars. The apparatus used for measuring the distances between the star images on the plates is an elaborate affair, made with extreme precision.

The procedure is to expose plates on a chosen star when it is near the meridian in the evening, and again, six months later, when it is near the meridian in the early morning. The programme for the year is mapped out in advance, and exposures are made whenever the sky is clear.

It should also be explained that the telescope is mounted so that it can follow a star by turning about an axis parallel to the axis of the earth, that it is driven by automatic mechanism to keep pace with the star and that a small visual telescope, fitted with cross wires, is fixed to the main telescope so that the observer can watch the star and correct any slight errors of motion of the telescope that may occur during the exposure. It is really not correct to say that the telescope keeps pace with the star; it is actually standing still while the earth rotates beneath it.

As we have seen, the method of parallax has been confirmed by independent methods within the confines of the solar system, and there is no reason to suppose that the validity of this method breaks down in regions beyond the solar system. The checks described in Chapter 3, whereby the results of parallax measurements within the solar system have been confirmed, are not applicable to the distances of the stars.

Assuming the validity of parallax among the stars, we can sum up the stage that we have reached in this investigation by saying that we know of no star nearer to us than about 300,000 times the distance of the sun, that most stars are much more distant than this, and that the vast majority are indeed utterly beyond the reach of the parallax method. The orbit of the earth is really not large enough. Astronomers (if any) on the superior planets are very much better off, although they would have to wait longer for the results – twelve of our years in the case of Jupiter; but the results would be five times as accurate. The Saturnian astronomers would have to wait thirty of our years, but would be rewarded by results nearly ten times more accurate than ours. Stars having a parallax of only 0″.08 as seen from the earth would have their distances measured as accurately as we have measured the distance of Proxima Centauri. The volume of space that they could explore by means of parallax measurements would be one thousand times as great as the volume accessible to us by this method.

CHAPTER V

MOVING CLUSTERS
AND THE DÖPPLER PRINCIPLE
BINARY STARS

MOVING CLUSTERS AND THE DÖPPLER PRINCIPLE

FORTUNATELY our resources do not end with the parallax method; there are various indirect methods by which the distances of more remote objects are measured, but before dealing with these mention must be made of two methods, unfortunately applicable only to a few stars, which are important because they do not depend on parallax at all – they could be employed even if the earth were not circling round the sun to provide us with our 180 million-mile base-line. They therefore provide very valuable checks on the parallax method.

What is a Moving Cluster? It has been mentioned already that the stars are described as 'fixed' stars only to distinguish them from the wandering planets, but that in fact they move among themselves; they are in movement across the sky in various directions and at various angular speeds – the 'proper motion' of the stars. Now if the proper motions of the more rapidly-moving stars in certain regions of the sky are plotted on a star-map, it is found that among all the random arrows indicating the directions of the proper motions some can be picked out which point towards a single spot. Compare Figure 23 and Figure 24. In the first of these there are a great many arrows representing all the stars in that particular area of sky which have accurately determined proper motions. The length of the arrow is proportional to the amount of the motion in each case – a star which is now at the bowstring end would (if its motion continued unchanged) be at the point of the arrow in, say, ten centuries from now.

This star map is purely imaginary – it does not represent any part of the actual sky.

Figure 24 shows only those few stars whose arrows all point at the same spot P. They constitute a moving cluster. At first sight it seems as if these stars were endowed with foresight and purpose, having at some time in the past decided among themselves to hold a meeting at P. This is obvious non-

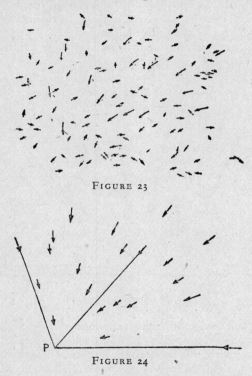

FIGURE 23

FIGURE 24

sense, and some other interpretation must be found. It is therefore assumed that they are moving along parallel paths, and that the apparent convergence is an effect of perspective.

This can be understood easily by considering the paths across the sky of a number of aircraft flying in formation away from us. Sometimes these paths are made visible by the condensation trails which were so familiar to us during the late war. Figure 25 shows a squadron of aircraft and their trails. Short transverse lines indicate the distances travelled in the same time by the units of this rather ragged formation. All the trails converge to a point X which is so distant that when the aircraft get there the whole squadron shrinks to a point. The convergence is an effect of perspective.

An observer in an aircraft flying very high would see these

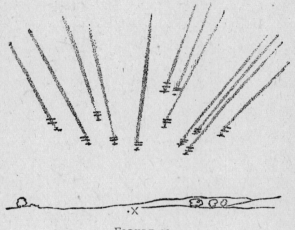

aircraft and their trails mapwise as shown in Figure 26, which also shows us stationed at O. All the trails are parallel, and the portions intercepted between the transverse lines are all equal, because the ground speeds of all the aircraft are equal.

Could we draw Figure 26 from observations made on the ground from O? We could if we knew the ground-speed of the aircraft, and if we took two photographs of them separated by a known interval of time. A cine film would give us just the information we require – a sequence of pictures taken at intervals of one twenty-fourth of a second · and we should need no assistance from condensation trails. If we made a composite print from two frames of the film, twenty-four frames apart, it would look like Figure 27. Lines drawn through the images intersect at X, which we identify from objects on the ground as bearing south–south-west, for example. We now know the bearing of the line A in Figure 26.

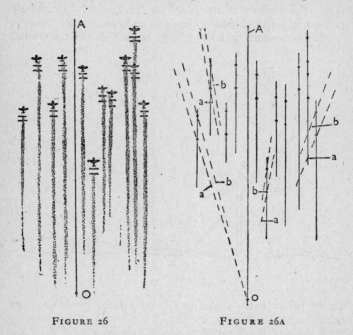

FIGURE 26   FIGURE 26A

All the aircraft are flying parallel to this line. We measure on the photograph (Figure 27) the angular distance between the point X and the point on the ground vertically beneath each aircraft. This enables us to draw the corresponding (dotted) lines on the map, Figure 26a. We know that each aircraft was somewhere on one of its lines (a) when the first frame was exposed, and somewhere on the other of its lines (b) at the time of the second exposure, one second later. Knowing that in one second the aircraft flew, say, 350 feet, we find the position on each pair of lines at which 350 feet, measured parallel to A, just fits between the two lines. This fixes the positions of each aircraft at the two instants, and we can measure on the map the distance of each aircraft from O at any instant – or rather the distance of the point on the ground immediately beneath it, which is what Figures 26 and 26a actually show.

All this depends on a knowledge of the speed of the aircraft

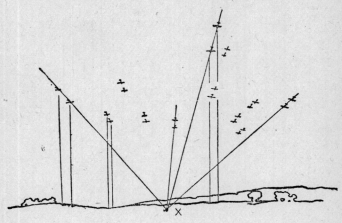

FIGURE 27

in feet per second – linear speed, not angular speed or speed of apparent travel across the sky. We can make little progress with the analogous problem of the moving cluster until we know the speed of the stars relative to the earth in miles or kilometres per second. Without this knowledge we can, it is true, draw a diagram similar to Figure 26a for each star in the cluster, but we do not know its scale. The position is the same as it was, in the case of the solar system, before the distance in miles or kilometres between the sun and the earth was known;

74

we could draw a picture of the solar system accurately to scale, but the *value* of the scale was unknown.

It happens that we can measure this speed (or rather one component of it) with comparative ease, by the aid of the 'Döppler principle' mentioned in the chapter heading. Döppler, of course, is the name of the physicist who enunciated the principle.

We are all thoroughly familiar with one effect of this Döppler principle. If we are standing on the platform when a fast train goes through with the whistle sounding, we hear the pitch of the whistle fall very appreciably as the engine passes. The pitch is high when the whistle is approaching us, and low when it is receding. When we recall that sound is a wave motion in the air the reason for this difference of pitch can easily be seen. Suppose the whistle (as heard by the driver) is vibrating the air 550 times per second. (In technical language, it has a frequency of 550 per second.) The speed of sound may be taken to be 1100 feet per second, so that in 1100 feet, measured from the whistle, there will be 550 equally-spaced waves. The length of each wave will therefore be 2 feet. When the whistle is approaching us at, say, 50 feet per second, it is catching up on the waves which it is causing. Each individual vibration is setting out from a point $\frac{50}{1100}$ foot, or slightly more than half an inch, nearer to us than the previous one. The wavelength is now that much less than 2 feet, and the frequency correspondingly higher. The speed of the sound through the air is the same (1100 feet per second) and as there are more of these shorter waves in 1100 feet, there are more per second. The pitch therefore sounds higher to us than it does to the driver; we judge the frequency to be 562.8 per second. The reverse argument shows why the pitch is lower, and by how much, when the whistle is receding. That is the Döppler principle.

Before applying this principle to the stars, let us return to our aircraft. We were supposed to know the speed of the aircraft, but nothing was said about how we knew it. We could measure it by means of whistles and tuning forks if there were no better way. Suppose each aircraft to carry a whistle of some definite pitch, say 550 vibrations per second, and that we have tuning forks or some equivalent means for determining the pitch of sounds. We could then determine the rise of pitch while the aircraft was approaching and the fall of pitch while it was receding, and this would obviously enable us to measure the speed of the aircraft in feet per second by using the above argument in reverse. Of course this will give us the true speed only if the pitch is determined while the aircraft is flying directly towards us or directly away from us. If it is not, what we shall have measured is the *component* of its speed along the line joining us to the aircraft, or in other words the rate at which its distance from us in a direct line is changing.

At the instant when an aircraft is directly overhead it is not changing its distance from us. It has ceased to approach and has not yet begun to recede. The same applies to an aircraft not flying directly overhead; at the instant when the line joining it to us is at right angles to its line of flight it is neither approaching nor receding, and the sound of its whistle, when it reaches us, will have the same pitch as is heard by the pilot. A short time before or after this instant the speed of approach or recession is small and the change of pitch of the sound as heard by us is also small. This will explain why, when we hear the whistle of the passing train from a point well back from the edge of the platform, the change of pitch as the whistle passes us is more gradual than it is when we are standing close to the edge. Another example of this effect was very noticeable in Southern England during the latter half of 1944. Flying bombs were propelled by jet reaction 'engines' which were from our present point of view organ pipes emitting a low-pitched musical note, albeit an impure, harsh note. Many people will recall the sudden fall of pitch of this note when a flying bomb passed directly overhead, and the much more gradual fall when the course of the bomb was well to one side. This came to be generally recognised as a method of judging whether an approaching bomb was likely to be dangerous or not, even by people who knew nothing of Döppler's principle.

If the pitch did not fall as the sound became louder one took a poor view of the situation. If the pitch fell slowly one felt much better.

Now let us apply this to the actual problem of the aircraft, and for practical reasons let us suppose that only one aircraft carries a whistle. In Figure 28 this aircraft is shown at the instant when the first photograph is taken. We determine the fall of pitch of the whistle at that instant, and we find that it corresponds to a speed of, say, 300 feet per second. But this

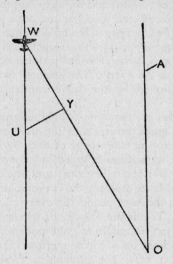

FIGURE 28

is only the speed at which the line O–W is lengthening at that instant. To determine the speed at which the aircraft is flying on its course parallel to A, we find a point Y, 300 millimetres from W on our diagram, draw a line Y–U perpendicular to O–W, cutting the aircraft's course at U. Then the speed of the aircraft along its course will be equal to the number of milli-metres in the length W–U.

As in similar cases dealt with in earlier chapters, the result is obtained in practice by calculation, not by measurement on a diagram; but, as before, the graphical method has been used herein for the sake of clearness.

Now it is time to return to the stars. They send us no sound, but they emit light, and in this light there are markers, as it were, which tell us the wave-length (or the frequency) of the light.

Light is a kind of wave motion and the same kind of relation exists between its frequency (the number of waves passing a given point per second) and its wave-length, as in the case of sound. As already mentioned, sound has a velocity of 1100 feet per second (under normal sea-level conditions) and therefore if the frequency is 550 the wavelength will be $\frac{1100}{550} = 2$ feet. The velocity is therefore the product of frequency and wave-length; $550 \times 2 = 1100$. The same is true of light; the frequency multiplied by the wave-length is equal to the velocity.

Wireless waves are the same as light except that the wave-length is very much greater and the frequency very much smaller. At the top of every page of the *Radio Times* the frequency of each transmitter is given in kilocycles per second (one kilocycle is 1,000 vibrations) and the wave-length is given in metres. If we multiply the two numbers together and by 1000, we get the same product in every case – 300,000,000 (within a little). This is the velocity of wireless waves (and of light) in metres per second, in round numbers. Thus the Home Service is broadcast on a wave-length of 342.1 metres at a frequency of 877 kc/s. The product of these two numbers (remembering that the 'k' stands for 1000) is 299,021,700. The Light Programme is broadcast on two wave-lengths – 1500 metres (200 kc/s) and 261.1 metres (1,149 kc/s) which multiplied together give respectively 300,000,000 and 300,003,900. Even the Third Programme conforms – $514.6 \times 583 = 300,011,800$ and $203.5 \times 1474 = 299,959,000$.

Light from a filament lamp or other white-hot solid body consists of a jumble of frequencies, of which our eyes are capable of seeing about one octave – that is to say, the frequency of the violet light is about twice that of the red light. In this octave there are all the frequencies (literally an infinite number) which can occur within its limits, and not merely the thirteen separate, well-defined frequencies occurring in the air of a room in which all the eight white keys and the five black keys of an octave are struck at the same time.

The light from the stars (including the sun) is different because certain definite frequencies are missing. They are absorbed by various substances present in a cool outer layer or 'skin' of the star, known as the chromosphere. These substances (hydrogen, calcium, iron, sodium and so on) are the same as those on the earth. Bits of these substances when heated emit light of frequencies exactly the same as those which are absorbed by them in the chromospheres of the stars. An instrument, called a spectroscope, containing glass prisms, spreads the starlight out into a rainbow-coloured band, called the spectrum, and in this spectrum the missing frequencies appear as narrow, dark lines.

We can also pass through the spectroscope light from a piece of iron, say, heated in an electric arc, and note whether the bright lines produced in this way agree in position with the corresponding dark lines in the star spectrum. If they correspond exactly we conclude that the star is neither approaching nor receding. If they do not correspond, but are displaced towards the red end of the spectrum (the low-frequency end) as compared with the bright lines from the piece of terrestrial iron, we conclude that the star is receding. If the displacement is towards the blue end (the high-frequency end), the star is approaching. Measurement of the displacement, and calculation, gives us the velocity of recession or approach as the case may be, in miles or kilometres per second (linear velocity, not angular) just as we were able to find the velocity of approach and recession of the locomotive by the change of pitch of its whistle. Velocities obtained in this way are known as line-of-sight or 'sightline' velocities. The term 'radial velocity' is sometimes used, but is best avoided as it is apt to lead to confusion. It must be made clear that the velocities of the stars are so very small compared with the velocity of light that the shift is only a very small fraction of the length of the spectrum.

Now it will be seen that in the case of the moving cluster we have all the data necessary to enable the distances of all the stars in the cluster to be determined by the method already explained for the aircraft. Instead of sound we use light; the velocities are many kilometres per second instead of a few hundred feet per second, the frequencies are many millions per second instead of five hundred or so, and the time intervals are centuries instead of seconds. In principle, however, the method is the same as that described above.

In the case of the aircraft we wanted to reconstruct the view, shown in Figure 26, as seen from a high-flying aircraft, and we therefore dealt with the positions and distances of the points on the ground immediately beneath the aircraft of the low-flying squadron. In the case of the stars, of course, the distances of the stars themselves are required and therefore each star in the cluster is dealt with separately on the basis of its true angular distance from the point P. Instead of a general 'map' such as Figure 26 or Figure 26a we should have to use a number of diagrams like Figure 28, one for each star, if we were solving the problem graphically.

It may have occurred to the reader that if there are moving clusters the members of which are apparently moving away from the point P it is not unreasonable to suppose that they are really moving outwards from that point, having perhaps been formed there by the bursting or fission of a very large star, or in some such way. Such a thing is not impossible but it is very unlikely. In all such cases the velocities measured by the spectroscope are found to be velocities of approach. If the outward motion were real, we should expect to find that in some cases some of the stars were receding from us, because they would be spreading out in all directions like splinters from an exploding bomb.

Distances obtained for the cluster stars by parallax measurements and other means are found to agree with those obtained by the method dealt with in this chapter. The two methods therefore check one another and the result of the check supports the validity of the assumption of parallel motion.

Sightline velocities obtained by means of the spectroscope serve as checks on distances within the solar system, additional to those already described in Chapter 3. The period of revolution of Venus round the sun is known. Its velocity of approach or recession relative to the earth can be measured with the spectroscope, and a simple calculation gives the circumference of its orbit in miles or kilometres, and therefore every other dimension in the solar system. Many years ago J. Evershed obtained in this way a value of the solar parallax which was thought to be too small at the time but which is in fair agreement with the value obtained recently by Spencer Jones from observations of Eros (Chapter 4).

The period of rotation of the sun about its axis is known. The velocities of approach and recession of points on the equator at opposite limbs of the sun can be measured, and this at once gives the value of the sun's circumference. As the earth is nearest to the sun in January and furthest away in July, it follows that it is receding from the sun in the first half of the year (most rapidly in April) and approaching it in the second half (most rapidly in October). An observer on the earth is moving towards the rising sun and moving away from the setting sun, by reason of the rotation of the earth. All these motions can be detected and measured by means of the spectroscope. The shifts of the spectrum lines caused by these motions of the earth relative to the sun are very small and therefore they do not give accurate values; but as far as they go they check and confirm the validity of the conclusions arrived at by other means.

This section must end with a confession. There is an error in the argument concerning Figure 28 which must now be put right. Sound travels much more slowly than light, and therefore when we *see* the aircraft at a certain point, the sound emitted by its whistle at that point has not yet reached us. Strictly, we ought to determine the position of the aircraft by listening instead of looking. In the case of the cluster stars we use the same agency – light – for determining position as for determining velocity, and therefore no error arises.

BINARY STARS

Now we come to our second chapter heading – binary stars.

If the components of a double star are observed to be in orbital revolution around one another, it is referred to as a binary star, to distinguish it from double stars in which no orbital motion has been detected and which may therefore consist of two stars widely separated but appearing close together because they are nearly in the same line of sight.

After a binary star has been observed throughout a complete revolution its apparent orbit can be drawn. It is assumed to begin with that the brighter component is fixed and that only the fainter companion moves. The orbits of some of these stars are seen broadside-on or nearly so – in other words the line of sight is perpendicular to the plane of the orbit. Others have orbits which are seen nearly edge-on – the line of sight is nearly in the plane of the orbit. When this is the case the spectroscope can tell us, by the displacement of the spectrum lines, the velocity of the companion in miles or kilometres per second – and not only that, but the velocity of the bright component as well. Being more massive, it does not move so fast or so far as the lighter component, but it moves nevertheless, just as the earth, although eighty times as massive as the moon, revolves in a small orbit owing to the attraction of the moon.

We know the time of one revolution of the binary, we know the velocity and therefore we can calculate the actual diameter of the orbit, just as we could calculate the diameter of the orbit of Venus from similar data. We can do this for both components, and therefore we can determine the real orbits of both components round their common centre of gravity – which enables us to compute the ratio between the masses of the two components, just as we found the ratio of the masses of the earth and the moon.

Moreover – and this is the important fact from our present

point of view – we can easily calculate the distance of the binary from us. From what has already been said in earlier chapters this will be obvious; we know the angular diameter of the orbit directly from the observations, we know its diameter in miles or kilometres, and the distance follows at once.

As an example, we will assume that the orbit is observed to be 5″ in angular diameter, and 100 astronomical units in actual diameter. As an object appears to have an angular diameter of 1″ when its distance is 206,265 times its linear or real diameter, the distance of this binary is $\frac{206,265}{5}$ times its real diameter, or $\frac{206,265}{5} \times 100 = 4,125,300$ astronomical units. This corresponds to a parallax of 0″.05 – one twentieth of a second of arc.

Now it will be clear that in deriving this distance we have not made any use at all of actual parallax measurements, either directly or indirectly. We could find the distance of a suitably-dimensioned binary star by the method described even if we had never measured the parallax of a single star. Like the moving clusters, therefore, the few binaries that are available for the purpose provide a check on the parallax method, and it is satisfactory to know that the results of the two methods agree whenever they can be directly compared.

The binary stars so far dealt with have components which can be seen separately in the telescope. There are vast numbers of binaries the components of which are so close together that they cannot be seen separately even in the most powerful telescopes. They were detected by the spectroscope, which the reader by this time will have concluded is a very powerful instrument of research. It is the same story – the shift of the spectrum lines revealing motion in the line of sight. In the spectra of some stars the lines are seen to be displaced alternately in opposite directions with a regular periodicity. In others, two different spectra are seen (often of two different types) which are sometimes merged with one another while at other times the lines are seen double, the doubling and the merging occurring with complete regularity. When the two spectra are of different types, the lines of one type are displaced towards the red at one period of doubling, while those of the other type are displaced towards the blue. At the next period of doubling this is reversed – the lines of the first-mentioned type are on the 'blue' side of those of the second type. These alternations are maintained perfectly regularly.

These displacements can mean only one thing – there are two stars revolving round one another. When there is only one spectrum, we conclude that the second star is so faint that its light is overpowered by that of its bright companion.

The number of stars the spectra of which show this kind of displacement or doubling is very large. It should be borne in mind that the orbits may be inclined at any angle to the line of sight – some broadside-on, some nearly edge-on and others at all possible inclinations – and only those whose orbits are inclined at relatively acute angles to the line of sight can be expected to show the effect of their motion in their spectra. It can be inferred, therefore, that a very high proportion of the stars are of this kind. They are known as spectroscopic binaries.

In general, nothing much can be made of the observations because the velocity deduced from the displacement of the spectrum lines may be any fraction whatever of the real orbital velocity, owing to the (unknown) inclination of the orbit plane to the line of sight.

There are some, however, whose orbits are so nearly edge on that each component passes between us and the other at every revolution. Even if the two components are of equal luminosity and size, this will cause a variation of the light reaching us, because when they are broadside-on to us we are getting light from both, while when either is directly in front of the other we are receiving light from only one. When one component, equal perhaps in size to the other (or even larger), is dimmer than the other, the diminution in the light reaching us is very great when the dim component is hiding the bright one, and only slight when the bright component is in front of the dim one. Stars of this type will be mentioned again in the next chapter.

These eclipsing binaries, as they are called, were first detected by their variable brightness, and the spectroscope has since supplied the explanation of their variable light. The important point to notice is that, because the eclipses occur, we can be sure that the orbit is edge-on to us (or very nearly so) and therefore that the velocities deduced from the Döppler displacement are the same as (or only slightly less than) the real velocities of the components in their orbits. This fact, in conjunction with a study of the light-curves (see Figure 29, page 90), has enabled astronomers to deduce a surprising amount of information about such binaries – the distance (in miles or kilometres) between the centres of the components, the combined mass of the components, the diameter of each of them, the exact inclination of the plane of the orbit to the line of sight and even the *shape* of the components, which in some cases are found to be egg-shaped, not spherical. All this, in spite of the fact that the star looks like a single point of light in the most powerful telescope! Truly the spectroscope is a worker of wonders.

Now unless we know the distance between the components in angular measure we cannot deduce the distance of such a binary by the method used for visual binaries – those whose components can be seen separately in the telescope. There is another way in which it can be done, however, namely by making use of what is known as the mass-luminosity relationship, discovered by Eddington. He found that all stars having any particular mass have the same intrinsic luminosity, and that there is a simple numerical relationship between mass and intrinsic luminosity which applies to all stars. This relationship was deduced from a study of binaries the distances of which had been measured, and therefore it is not independent of parallax measurements. However, it does enable us to find the intrinsic luminosities (and therefore the distances, as will be explained in the next chapter) of the components of any eclipsing binary even if it is too distant to have a measurable parallax.

CHAPTER VI

INDIRECT METHODS OF MEASURING
STELLAR DISTANCES

THE various indirect methods have this much in common; they are all based on the detection of some feature of *uniformity* among the stars whose distances have been determined by measuring their parallaxes. As soon as an appreciable number of reliable parallaxes had been obtained the search for such features began. The principle can best be made clear by taking a hypothetical case. Suppose it had been found that among the stars of known distances the apparent brightness varied inversely as the square of the distance, so that one star, twice as far away as another, was only one quarter as bright, while one three times as far was one ninth as bright, and so on. We could then be certain that these stars would all appear equally bright when seen from the same distance and that in fact they were all of the same intrinsic brightness – the same candle-power. If there were no exceptions to this rule among the stars of known distance we should be fairly safe in assuming that it was true also of stars too distant to have measurable parallaxes. Then indeed astronomers would be in clover, because all they would have to do would be to measure the apparent brightness of every star, and simple arithmetic would give their distances – subject, of course, to the assumption that what is true of some stars is true of all.

It is not, alas, so simple as that. Stars are of all degrees of intrinsic brightness and only in a very broad statistical sense can it be said that fainter stars are more distant than bright stars.

The first feature of uniformity to be discovered was that stars having a certain definite characteristic in their spectra are of the same intrinsic brightness, within limits. It has already been explained that when the various frequencies in the light from a star are spread out into a band by means of a spectroscope, it is found that certain frequencies are missing. In the spectrum of the sun these missing frequencies are many thousands in number and they appear as dark lines crossing the band, some very dark and prominent, others fainter, closely bunched in some places and more widely scattered in others. They correspond to the various elements – hydrogen, helium, iron, magnesium and the rest. Thus for example hydrogen is represented by a series of lines, very close together in the ultra-violet and getting further apart towards the red end. Calcium (the basis of limestone and chalk on the earth) is responsible for two extremely wide, prominent lines in the extreme violet. The lines due to iron are scattered throughout the length of the spectrum.

Now the number of elements the lines of which can be identified in the spectrum of a star varies from star to star. In some, the lines of hydrogen are predominant; in others they are absent and the prominent lines are due, not to elements, but to compounds – oxides of some of the metals. The sun's spectrum is an intermediate type in which the hydrogen lines, though present, are not dominant and most of the lines are due to various metals. This does not mean that a star showing only the hydrogen lines contains nothing but hydrogen and that another whose spectrum shows no hydrogen lines contains no hydrogen. These differences in the spectra are due to differences in the physical conditions – temperature and pressure. A 'hydrogen' star is at a very high temperature and it is this that prevents the lines of other elements from appearing. Again, compounds such as metallic oxides can exist only at comparatively low temperatures.

Most people who have not had the opportunity of studying the subject assume that the sun is very hot because it is burning, and they are astonished (and not a little sceptical) when a physicist tells them that the sun is far too hot to burn. Yet this is perfectly true. Combustion, or burning, always results in the formation of compounds of elements such as hydrogen and carbon with the element oxygen. When coal gas burns, the hydrogen enters into combination with the oxygen of the air to form the oxide of hydrogen – water, each molecule of which consists of two atoms of hydrogen and one atom of oxygen – H_2O, to use the chemist's shorthand. Coke (which is mostly carbon) when burnt combines with oxygen to form carbon dioxide (CO_2) each molecule of which consists of one atom of carbon and two atoms of oxygen. If either of these compounds is heated to a sufficiently high temperature it dissociates, that is, splits up again into its original elements – hydrogen and oxygen in the case of water, carbon and oxygen in the case of carbon dioxide. The same is true of other chemical compounds, apart from oxides. The temperature of the sun is higher than the dissociation temperature of nearly all chemical compounds. The elements cannot combine with one another. The sun *is* too hot to burn.

Returning to the stars generally, close study of the spectra of stars of known distances, the *apparent* brightnesses of which were of course also known, showed that the intrinsic brightness bore a definite relationship to the ratio between the intensities of certain lines in the spectrum. Let us take this by stages. It is easy to see that if we know the apparent brightnesses or magnitudes of a number of stars, and if we also know their distances, we can calculate their intrinsic brightnesses – their absolute magnitudes, to use the astronomer's term. The absolute magnitude of a star is defined as the magnitude (apparent brightness) that it would have if seen from a distance of 10 parsecs. It is clear that a star 5 parsecs away from us would appear only one-quarter as bright at 10 parsecs, the apparent brightness being inversely proportional to the square of the distance. Hence it is possible, by simple arithmetic, to say how bright the various stars would appear if they were all at a distance of 10 parsecs.

Now it was found that in the spectra of all stars having a certain absolute magnitude the intensities of these tell-tale spectrum lines were in a certain definite proportion or ratio (for example one of them might be twice as intense or dark as another) while in the spectra of all stars having another value of the absolute magnitude this proportion or ratio was different; the first-mentioned line would be for example three times as intense as the other. Here then we have a feature of uniformity among the stars – not so simple as that imagined in the first paragraph of this chapter, but of the same kind. All we have to do is to photograph the spectrum of a star too distant to have a measurable parallax, measure the ratio of intensities of these lines, and measure its apparent brightness or magnitude. The ratio of intensities will tell us how bright the star would appear – what its magnitude would be – at a distance of 10 parsecs, and from this, and its *observed* magnitude, we can compute its distance.

Astronomers prefer to express stellar distances as parallaxes, even when no parallax has been (or could be) measured. Parallaxes which are inferred in this way from the ratio of intensities of spectrum lines are referred to as *spectroscopic parallaxes*, and directly-measured parallaxes are sometimes called *trigonometrical parallaxes;* but when the word 'parallax' is used alone, without qualification, it is to be understood to mean the directly measured quantity.

Another very important indirect method depends upon a different type of uniformity among stars of a particular kind – the cepheid variables. Most stars shine with a constant light, but a proportion of them are variable in brightness. These variable stars have been carefully studied for a long time and different types of variability have been recognised. One type has already been mentioned in Chapter 5 (the eclipsing binary type) the components of which revolve round one another in an orbit which happens to be 'edge-on' to the earth, so that each component periodically passes in front of the other. If one of them happens to be appreciably brighter than the other, its light is dimmed appreciably when its duller companion passes in front of it. There is another diminution of brightness, much less in amount, when the bright component passes in front of the dull one, because then only the bright one is sending us light, whereas at other times the light of the dull one is reaching us as well.

Other variable stars behave irregularly; neither the intervals between maxima (the times of maximum brightness) nor the brightness at successive maxima are equal. They are classed as irregular variables.

The type which we are interested in (the cepheid variables) show variations which recur at absolutely regular intervals and are constant in amount, but they can be distinguished from the eclipsing variables by means of the spectroscope. This must be made clear.

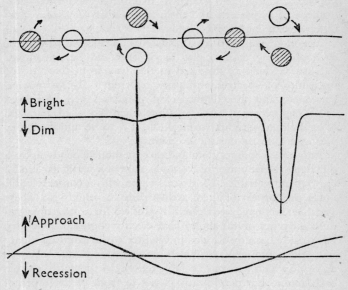

FIGURE 29

In Chapter 5 it was explained how the sightline velocity of a star could be found by measuring the minute shift of the lines in its spectrum. Let us see how this operates in the case of an eclipsing binary. In Figure 29 are shown four positions of the two components, one of which is shown shaded to indicate that it is the dull one. Underneath is a graph or chart showing the consequent variations in the light received by us. Underneath this again is another graph or chart showing the variations in the sightline velocity. Here it should be pointed out that when one component is very much brighter than the other only the spectrum of the bright one can be seen, that of the dull one being swamped. The varying sightline velocity is therefore that of the bright component.

The point to notice is that the sightline velocity is zero at times of minimum light and a maximum at intervening times when the light is a maximum, this maximum velocity being alternately a velocity of approach and a velocity of recession.

Now there is a moderately bright star, in the constellation Cepheus, called δ Cephei, which is regularly variable in a period of about five and one third days, being rather more than three times as bright at maximum as it is at minimum. The variability of this star (and of several others) was first detected by an Englishman, Goodricke, in the late eighteenth century. It is easily visible to the naked eye and its fluctuations can be followed without a telescope. It is much better to use binoculars, however, because there is another fairly bright star (not variable) very close to it which cannot be seen separately with the naked eye. With binoculars the two can be separated and the constant brightness of the companion serves as a convenient standard. δ Cephei itself can be seen sometimes equal to the companion in brightness and sometimes much fainter.

It was assumed for a long time that this star was an eclipsing binary, but when it was studied with the spectroscope it was found that the variations in its sightline velocity were not consistent with this interpretation. Figure 30 will make this clear when compared with Figure 29.

The star is approaching us with greatest velocity when its light is brightest and receding from us fastest when its light is a minimum. It is neither approaching nor receding when its light is of intermediate brightness. It is impossible to draw diagrams, such as the upper series in Figure 29, showing two stars revolving round one another, which will make sense of the graph of sightline velocity.

This star was therefore a puzzle to astronomers and even now no completely convincing explanation of its behaviour is forthcoming. The most plausible theory is that the star is not moving towards and away from us as a whole but is expanding and contracting, like a toy balloon blown up and deflated alternately, the observed sightline velocity being that of the surface of the star facing us.

The difficulty about the 'pulsation' theory is this. Obviously the sightline velocity is zero when the star is fully blown out and when it is fully 'deflated'. We should expect it to be brightest when it is largest, but it is not; it is brightest when it

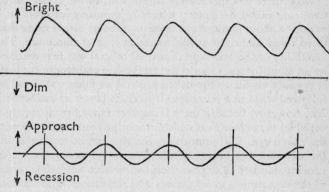

FIGURE 30

is half blown up and dimmest when it is half deflated – and it is about as bright when largest as it is when smallest. It has to be confessed that we do not fully understand the odd behaviour of this star.

Now in course of time other stars were found which behave in the same way. Even among the naked-eye stars there are about a dozen of them, and of course many more among the vast number of stars too faint to be seen without a telescope. They are the cepheid variables, named after the first of them to be studied – δ Cephei.

It was an American lady astronomer, Miss Leavitt, who

took the first step in detecting the important uniformity of the cepheid variables. In the southern sky, invisible from the British Isles, are two patches of misty light, looking like detached parts of the Milky Way or Galaxy. They are called the Greater and Lesser Magellanic Clouds, after Magellan, the fifteenth century navigator, who first drew attention to them. They are also known as the Nubecula Major and the Nubecula Minor. Miss Leavitt made a detailed study of the stars and other objects in the Lesser Magellanic Cloud. She found that all the well-known types of stars were represented, including a number of cepheid variables. It is important to appreciate that because this Cloud is of small angular size we can be certain that all the objects in it are very nearly at the same distance from us. The distance may be unknown, but it is the same (within about one per cent) for every part of the Cloud. Consequently, if two stars in it look equally bright, they are equal in intrinsic brightness.

Miss Leavitt found that there was a simple relation between the periods of the variation and the apparent brightnesses of all the cepheid variables in the Cloud, and therefore between the periods of the variation and the intrinsic brightnesses or absolute magnitudes, because they are all at very nearly the same distance from us. This relation, roughly speaking, is that the brighter the star, the longer the period.

The full significance of this fact was soon appreciated. Hertzsprung, a Danish astronomer, pointed out that, assuming that all cepheids everywhere were alike in this respect (in other words, assuming that the cepheids in the Lesser Magellanic Cloud are a fair sample of all cepheids) then we had a means of determining the distance of every one of them, once the distance of any one of them is known. Remember that although we know that the cepheids in the Cloud are all at the same distance, we do not yet know what that distance is.

There is no very exact analogy with the cepheid characteristic among familiar things, but perhaps we can imagine one. Most people are familiar with an unfortunate habit of badly-adjusted incandescent gas lamps; they are apt to bob up and down with a definite, regular period. Lamps on railway station platforms seem to be specially prone to this behaviour. Some of them have a short period (two or three ups and downs per second) while others are more leisurely. It is highly improbable that there is any definite connection or relation between the candle-power of the lamp and the period of its variation, but we can assume that there is – that the brighter the lamp, the slower the periodic variation of its light.

It is easy to see that if this were so we should have a rough-and-ready means of judging how far away such a lamp is. We are hurrying to catch a train at a country station which a passer-by has told us is 'not far'. We look at the bobbing lamps on the station platform and judge their candle-power by the rate at which they bob. Then we can judge how far we are from the station by noting how bright they look. If they are bobbing slowly, with a long period, and look dim, we know that we must hurry, because the lamps are really bright and their dimness is due to distance. If they are bobbing quickly and look dim we know that the station is not far away because the dimness is due more to low candle-power than to distance.

If lamps having this property were at all common we should very quickly learn how to judge distances in this way and would do so almost without thinking.

Returning to the cepheids, it is unfortunate that not one of them is near enough to us to have a large, and therefore accurately determined, parallax. The accuracy of the method based on this period-luminosity relationship is therefore not very high from one point of view, but it is very accurate for determining relative distances. For example if two clusters of stars both contain cepheids, we can tell accurately how many times more distant one is than the other; but the actual distances are rather more uncertain. On the other hand, taken as a class their intrinsic brightness is very high, and they are therefore visible even at great distances. Hence they can be used for estimating distances at which spectroscopic parallaxes are not available. The magnitude and period of a cepheid can easily be determined even if it is far too faint to afford a measurable spectrum.

There is another type of star which is also very useful as a gauge of distance, namely the extremely hot, bluish-white stars in the spectra of which the lines of helium are dominant. They are remarkably uniform in their intrinsic brightness – their absolute magnitudes do not differ very much. In fact they make a fair approach to the state of affairs imagined in the first paragraph of this chapter; if two stars of this type look equally bright, they are at about the same distance from us, while if one is one quarter as bright as another, then its distance is about twice as great, and so on. They are intrinsically very bright and they can therefore be used for estimating very great distances. They are known as B-type stars.

All such methods which depend on the magnitudes of the stars – their apparent brightness – are valid only if space is completely transparent. If it is not, if some of the light is lost by absorption on its way to us, then our measurements of magnitude are too low and the distances inferred from them are too great. We know that this absorption does take place, and we can detect it and allow for it. The absorption is due to dust in interstellar space and, like dust and smoke in our atmosphere, it produces more effect on violet and blue light than on green, yellow and red. Very distant stars, in some parts of the sky, look redder than they should do, and the amount of reddening tells us the amount of light lost by absorption.

It may be asked how we know what they would look like if there were no absorption. The answer is given by the spectroscope. Stars differ in colour – some are red like a glowing coal in the fire, some are yellow, some yellowish-white like the sun, others pure white and yet others bluish-white. These differences are due to temperature; the red stars are the coolest and the bluish-white ones are the hottest, as one would expect. Stars of any given temperature, and of a colour appropriate to that temperature, have a definite type of spectrum – the absorption lines have a definite, recognisable pattern. The hottest stars of all show very strongly the absorption lines of helium. If therefore we see a star with this type of spectrum which looks yellowish-white or yellow, instead of bluish-white as it should, we know that the yellowish colour is due to absorption in space of a proportion of the violet and blue components of the star's light, and we know that it looks dimmer than it should.

This again is something with which we are familiar enough in our daily life. If we see distant street-lamps looking yellowish or reddish, we know that there is mist or fog in the air, and we are not surprised that they also look dimmer than usual.

The reddening of the light of stars by interstellar dust is not the same in all parts of the sky – some regions of space are more 'dusty' than others. We therefore have a means of detecting the dusty, light-absorbing regions and getting some idea of their location, distance and extent.

The word 'absorption' is used in two different senses in the last paragraph but two. The lines in the spectrum are due to absorption of single frequencies by the photosphere of the star. The absorption by dust in space is a general absorption extending over all frequencies, but more strongly in the higher frequencies – violet and blue – than in the lower – yellow and red.

To make matters still more confusing, we are here obliged to mention that absorption of single frequencies also takes place in the spaces between the stars. These spaces contain atoms and molecules in addition to dust particles. In fact interstellar space is not an absolute vacuum; it is a mixture of gases at a very low pressure, the pressure and the density being so extremely low that in all probability there are only two or three atoms in each cubic inch.

There are, however, a great many inches between us and the more remote stars, and it is not altogether surprising that in certain circumstances these atoms make their presence evident in the spectra of very remote stars. It has already been mentioned that calcium is responsible for two very prominent lines in the solar spectrum and the spectra of many stars. Calcium atoms seem to be much more obstructive than others, and the relatively few atoms of calcium in the extremely tenuous gas which fills the interstellar spaces are able to cause their characteristic absorption lines to appear in the spectra of the distant stars.

We are being wise after the event in giving this account of 'inter-stellar calcium', as it is called. At first the observations were extremely puzzling. When the shifts of spectrum lines were measured to determine the sightline velocities of the stars, it was found that in many cases all the lines were displaced except the calcium lines, while in other cases the calcium lines were displaced, but not so much as the other lines.

The explanation, first given by Evershed, that these observations could be accounted for by calcium 'gas' in space, was at first rejected as improbable; but later observations, notably by J. S. Plaskett at Victoria, British Columbia, left no doubt that this was indeed true. It was recognised that in many cases the calcium lines appeared in the spectra of stars which ought not to have such lines. Stars having spectra in which the lines should appear were the ones in which the lines were displaced, but not to the same extent as the remainder of the lines. The explanation is simple – the 'interstellar' lines are superimposed on the star's own calcium lines and because the displacement due to the star's motion in the line of sight is never great enough to separate the two pairs of lines clearly, they merely appear slightly broadened. The centres of these composite, broadened lines are obviously not so much displaced by the motion in the line of sight as those lines which are due to the star's chromosphere alone.

These effects can evidently be used as a rough-and-ready gauge of distance, because the greater the distance, the more intense is the interstellar calcium absorption.

Some writers on astronomical subjects, particularly in the daily press, confuse matters by referring to a displacement of spectrum lines towards the red or low-frequency end as a reddening of the light. This is quite wrong; the light is not reddened at all. Even if a star were receding from us so fast that a line, ordinarily found in the blue part of the spectrum, were to appear in the red region, the light as a whole would not necessarily be reddened, because a large region of the ultra-violet, normally invisible, would be displaced into the visible region to take the place of the normally blue light which has become red.

There are many statistical methods of estimating stellar distances. They tell us nothing about the distances of single stars, but they are nevertheless very useful in some types of investigations. The simplest of all is that based on magnitude – that is, apparent brightness. The stars are of all intrinsic luminosities over a wide range, but if we take sufficiently large numbers these variations cancel out. The faint, closely-spaced stars of the Milky Way are more distant than the widely-scattered bright stars. This conclusion is not vitiated by the fact that there are a few intrinsically very faint stars near to us which are inadvertently counted in as belonging to the Milky Way, nor by the fact that a very distant nova (a star temporarily emitting many thousands of times the normal amount of light) may be counted among the nearer stars.

By taking averages of the magnitudes of large numbers of stars in various parts of the Milky Way, the relative distances of these various parts can be assessed with confidence.

Another statistical method, applicable to the stars relatively near to us, is based on the fact, already mentioned, that the solar system is in motion relative to the general mass of these stars. The spectroscope shows far more stars approaching than receding in one part of the sky, and far more receding than approaching in the part of the sky directly opposite. This is what we should expect to find if we walked across a large space in which many people were themselves walking in every direction, at various speeds, with people standing still here and there. Speaking generally, we should be getting nearer to most of the people in front of us, and getting further away from most of those behind us. There would be many exceptions, but in general that is what we should find. Also, the people on either side of our track would mostly fall behind – not all, but on the average there would be a backward trend.

The real point, however, is that those people on either side of us would not fall behind equally fast. Again on the average, those nearer to us would fall behind faster than those further away – we could keep anyone a long way away in view for a long time without having to turn our heads much; but to keep someone close to us in view we should have to turn our heads very quickly. By such observations we could tell which of the people on the average were near to us and which of them were distant. This seems silly as well as obvious, because we can tell more certainly by other means. But this does not apply to the stars – we cannot tell at a glance which are near and which are distant.

It is by this time completely obvious that if we measure the proper motions of large numbers of stars at the sides of our path (the sun's way, as it is called), those with large 'backward' proper motions are on the average nearer to us than those with small proper motions.

The advantage of this method is that it improves with time. The solar system moves about 380 million miles in a year among its neighbours and of course in ten years it has moved ten times that distance. If photographs are taken at intervals of twenty years, the stars will have fallen behind by considerable amounts, which can be measured easily without much error. In this respect (but only in this respect) the method is vastly superior to the ordinary parallax method, which is restricted to a movement of the earth of only 93,000,000 miles. It is vastly inferior in that it tells us nothing about individual stars; it can give us only statistical information – information about large numbers, among which the individuals are averaged.

We are now in a position to review the subject of stellar distances. The basic method is that of parallax. This method has been found to be valid within the solar system and there is no reason whatever to doubt its validity in the spaces beyond. On the other hand there is no possibility of direct proof – that is, of course, inherent in the problem. The two independent checks that are available, the moving-cluster method and the visual binary method (Chapter 5), provide confirmation which will convince all but the most sceptical.

The indirect methods are extensions of the parallax method and they stand or fall with it. They involve the assumption that a stellar feature, shown to be a feature of uniformity among stars of known distance, is also a feature of uniformity among stars of unknown distance. This is certainly reasonable, and we are quite accustomed to assumptions of this kind in ordinary life. Among the stars, we have the further safeguard that the assumptions underlying the various methods are independent of one another and therefore can be used as mutual checks. Thus, for example, the period-luminosity relation among the cepheids is quite independent of the spectrum feature on which spectroscopic parallaxes are based. When they lead to identical results it is hard to remain sceptical.

Every opportunity that presents itself is taken to apply these mutual checks. From time to time discrepancies have appeared, but further observations have always shown that the discrepancies were unreal and have strengthened the reliance placed by astronomers on the various methods that they use.

The result of the application of the methods described is a self-consistent scheme – it 'hangs together'. It is unlikely that any new facts that may come to light will bring about any radical change in this scheme, but the work is by no means finished. We may be certain that new methods will be devised, that the accuracy of observations will be improved and that as time goes on the details of the picture will be progressively filled in.

CHAPTER VII

SUMMING UP THE GALACTIC SYSTEM

THE most casual inspection of the sky reveals that the stars are more thickly set along the Milky Way, or Galaxy, and more thinly scattered in directions at right angles to it. Telescopic and photographic observations, which reveal thousands of times as many stars as can be seen by the naked eye, confirm this abundantly.

William Herschel was the first to count the numbers of stars in different parts of the sky in a systematic way – not, of course, the whole number of stars visible in his telescopes, but the numbers in small areas uniformly distributed over the sky. It is a system of sampling, in fact. This work was done in the latter part of the eighteenth and the early part of the nineteenth centuries.

Herschel was a most remarkable man, being endowed with tremendous energy, a brilliant intellect and manual skill of a high order. He put this latter gift to good use by making large numbers of reflecting telescopes, including one with a mirror four feet in diameter – far larger than any that had been made up to that time. We will defer for the present an explanation of what a reflecting telescope is; but it must be explained that the larger the diameter of the objective, whether it is a lens or mirror, the fainter the stars that it will show. Herschel's mirrors did not reflect such a high proportion of the light as a lens will transmit; but nevertheless his largest mirror, four feet in diameter, reflected four times as much light as a mirror only two feet in diameter, and would therefore show stars only one quarter as bright.

What Herschel did was not merely to count the numbers of stars in his sample areas with one telescope, but to make such counts with apertures of different diameters. This gave him valuable additional information. If we count, say, a hundred stars in a given patch of sky with a telescope of six inches aperture, we might reasonably expect to be able to count four hundred in the same patch with a telescope of twelve inches aperture, which has four times the area of the six-inch telescope. If we could repeat this, doubling the diameter of the aperture (and quadrupling its area) each time, would the number of stars visible also be quadrupled each time? The answer is yes, if the average spacing of the stars (the number in a given volume of space) does not fall off as we reach further out into space with our progressively larger telescopes. When we have made the largest telescope we can (and Herschel could not make one larger than four feet) our probing into space has reached a limit; and if we have found no falling off in the spacing of the stars up to that limit, we can do no more.

Herschel found that there was no such falling off in star spacing – no thinning out of the stars with increasing distance – in the Galaxy, but that they thinned out perceptibly in regions near the poles of the Galaxy where even to the naked eye the stars seem to be sparse.

These observations led him to believe that the system of stars was not infinite in extent, that even along the Galaxy there was a limit beyond which there would be no more stars; while in other directions he had the plainest evidence that the limit was much nearer.

He pictured the stars as occupying a space shaped something like a bath bun – a flattened, roughly circular shape – with the sun somewhere near the middle. The stars, in general, were uniformly distributed throughout most of this space, but thinned out gradually near its confines. We, looking out from the middle of the bun, would naturally see more stars, more closely set, in directions towards the edges of the bun, than we do looking towards the top or bottom of the bun. The Galaxy is thus explained, not as a separate and distinct ring of stars girdling the nearer stars, but as the natural outcome of our situation inside a much flattened, though substantially uniform, swarm of stars. This swarm is referred to as the Galactic System.

This system has no definite dimensions. It thins out gradually in all directions, so that one cannot say of any assigned boundary that it includes all the stars and other objects belonging to the system. Very roughly, its diameter is about 30,000 parsecs, or 100,000 light-years.

There are other things besides stars in this system – there are large clouds of obscuring dust and gases which dim the light of the stars beyond them, or even hide them altogether. These clouds are very evident in Plates I, II and III. Here and there these clouds are caused to glow by radiation from stars within them, much as our atmosphere is excited to luminosity by emanations from the sun, so that we see the Northern lights. The glow, visible in telescopes as a greenish light, was a puzzle for many years, for the spectroscope showed that it was due mainly to a few bright lines (single frequencies) which did not seem to correspond to the frequencies emitted by any substance known on the earth. We know now, however, that they are due to nitrogen and oxygen – the familiar air that we breathe – but at such a low density that their atoms do not behave at all in the same way as they do when crowded close together, as they are on the earth.

Herschel saw these obscuring clouds, but he did not recognise them as such; he thought they were actual gaps in the stars – vacant spaces through which he looked into outer space. He did, however, notice that these starless regions were associated with the glowing patches (known as nebulæ); when he came across a blank region in the course of his 'sweeps' of the sky, he called to his assistant who was taking notes – 'prepare for nebulæ'. Plate III shows a striking example of this effect.

There are also clusters of stars. These are among the most beautiful objects to be seen in the sky. Some of them are circular in shape and exquisitely symmetrical – the globular clusters. Others are irregular and unsymmetrical. One can get a very good idea of the appearance of a globular cluster by sprinkling salt on a piece of black paper, so that the grains are thickly spaced at the centre and thin out gradually in all directions. The grains of salt, differing in size, simulate the differing brilliance of the stars in the cluster. One such cluster is shown in Plate IV.

Many of these globular clusters contain numbers of cepheids, and these have enabled the distances of the clusters to be determined. It is found that all the cepheids in any cluster (which of course are all the same distance from us) have the same period-luminosity relation which was found originally for those in the Lesser Magellanic Cloud – a striking example of the uniformity found throughout the galactic system and strong support for the validity of the method of determining distances which is based on this relation.

The obscuring clouds occur most abundantly along the track of the Galaxy. They are densest in one particular region of the Galaxy, in the constellations of Sagittarius and Scorpio. This region also contains the brightest parts of the Galaxy, and there is a strong impression that if the obscuring clouds could be removed, still brighter parts would be revealed. Plates I and II show the appearance well.

In the British Isles this part of the Galaxy does not rise very far above the horizon, and consequently it does not appear to us very much brighter or more striking than the parts which we see higher in the sky. In more southerly latitudes, however, it is seen to better advantage and its pre-eminence is apparent.

The sun is not in the centre of the system. It is roughly half way out towards the edge, but quite near to the central plane – about in the middle of the thickness of the bun. The centre of the system lies in the direction of the bright star-concentrations in Sagittarius and Scorpio, where also are found the densest dust-clouds.

The stars comprising this system number many thousands of millions; they are countless. They are of all sizes, but their masses do not differ very much among themselves. The range of size is enormous; many stars are known which, if they could

Plate I. The Galaxy in Centaurus and Scorpio (*W. H. Steavenson*)

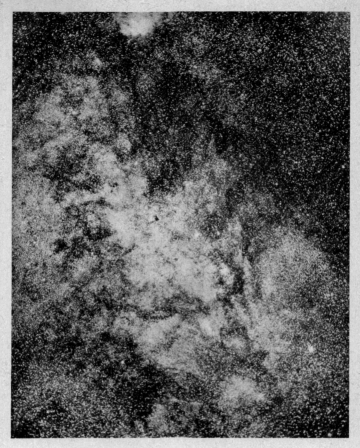

Plate II. Star Clouds in Sagittarius (*Barnard*)

Plate III. Gaseous nebulae and obscuring clouds near
ρ Ophiuchi (*Barnard*)

Plate IV. Globular Cluster M13 in Hercules (*J. S. Plaskett*)

Plate V. Spiral Nebula M31 (NGC 224) (*Ritchey*)

Plate VI. Spiral Nebula M31 (NGC 224) central part (*Humason*)

Plate VII. (right) Nebula NGC 4565 (*Ritchey*)

Plate VIII. Nebula NGC 4594 (*Mount Wilson Observatory*)

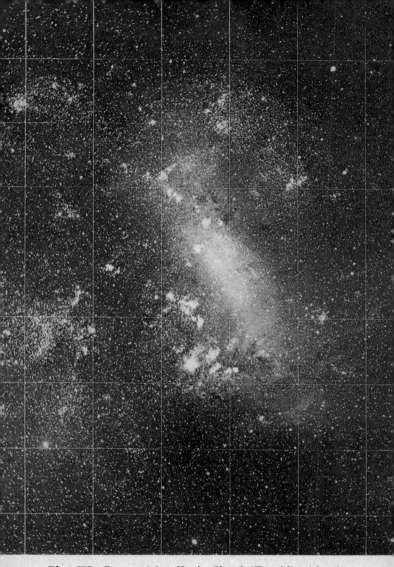

Plate IX. Greater Magellanic Cloud (*Franklin Adams*)

Plate X. Lesser Magellanic Cloud (*Harvard Observatory*)

Plate XI. Nebula of Normal Spiral type (NGC 5236)
(*Mount Wilson Observatory*)

Plate XII. Nebula of Barred Spiral type (NGC 5850)
(*Mount Wilson Observatory*)

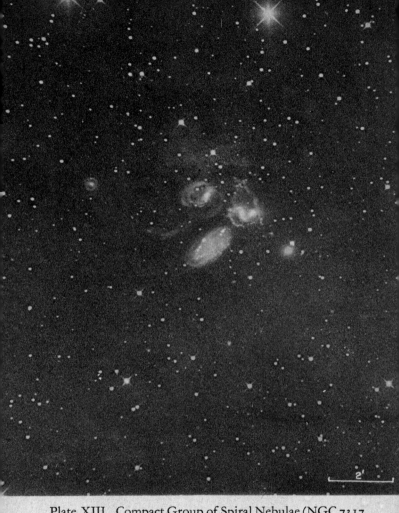

Plate XIII. Compact Group of Spiral Nebulae (NGC 7317, 7318, 7319 and 7320) (*Mount Wilson Observatory*)

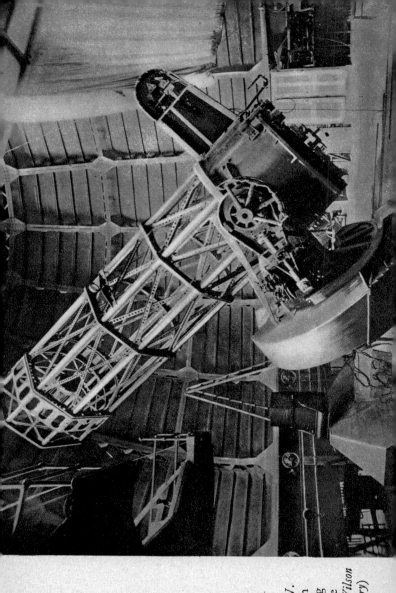

Plate XIV.
Sixty-inch
Reflecting
Telescope
(*Mount Wilson
Observatory*)

Plate XV. Hundred-inch Reflecting Telescope
(*Mount Wilson Observatory*)

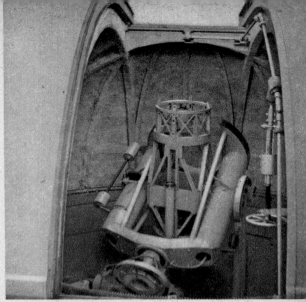

Plate XVI. Model of two-hundred-inch
Reflecting Telescope (*J. V. Thomson*)
Plate XVII. Two-hundred-inch mirror
in optical workshop (*J. V. Thomson*)

5'

Plate XVIII. Spiral Nebula M33 (NGC 598)
(*Mount Wilson Observatory*)

suddenly replace the sun, would engulf not only the earth, but Mars as well. Such stars are not particularly massive, and therefore their density is very small. In fact, throughout most of their volume the density is probably less than the density of air in the most perfect 'vacuum' that we can produce on the earth. At the other end of the scale are stars as massive as the sun but not much larger than the earth – so dense, in consequence, that a ton of their substance occupies a volume no larger than a match-box.

The temperatures of the stars also vary over a wide range. Some are so hot that they are a stage beyond white heat – they are 'blue hot'. Others are as cool as the molten iron in a blast furnace, and there is evidence of stars still cooler; too cool to emit visible light at all. These temperatures refer to the surfaces of the stars; in their interiors the temperatures are very much higher – many millions of degrees centigrade.

In all these respects (size, mass, temperature) the sun is completely undistinguished; it is of medium size, medium mass and medium temperature. It is classified, unflatteringly, as a G-type dwarf. There are so many more of its kind than of any other kind that if we could view the system from a very great distance and photograph its spectrum, it would closely resemble that of the sun. We cannot take much pride in our particular star, with which our fate is so indissolubly bound.

Although, if we take a sufficiently comprehensive view, we can regard the stars as uniformly scattered throughout the system, this is true only in a statistical sense; there is considerable clustering. The clusters are of all types, ranging from the compactly crowded globular clusters to comparatively loosely-associated, straggling assemblages. Our sun is a member of one of these latter.

The whole system is rotating, not as a solid body rotates, but rather as the solar system might be said to rotate as a whole by reason of the revolutions of the planets round the sun – all in the same direction but in different periods. It may be noted here that astronomers (unlike engineers) distinguish sharply between rotation and revolution. A movement like that of a wheel or a spinning top is described as rotation, while a movement like that of a weight whirled round on the end of a string, or of a rider on a merry-go-round, is described as revolution. The earth *rotates* once a day and *revolves* round the sun once a year.

The period of revolution of any star round the centre of the galactic system is of course extremely long; it is reckoned in hundreds of millions of years. No very precise figures can be given; it is only a few years since the fact of this rotation has been established and it may be a long time before the period of revolution of the sun, for example, is known with any certainty. It may be about two hundred million years.

The average distance between any two stars (binary stars being counted as single stars) is very great compared with the dimensions of the stars themselves. The diameter of the sun is 864,000 miles, a distance traversed by light in slightly more than four and a half seconds. Light takes about four and a half years to travel from the sun to its nearest neighbour, Proxima Centauri. Thus the distance between these two stars is about 32,000,000 times the diameter of one of them. This could be represented, in model form, by two ping-pong balls 750 miles apart.

In the globular clusters the stars are closer together than this, but even there the spacing of the stars is enormously greater than the size of any of them.

The galactic system therefore is mostly empty space (empty, that is, apart from the extremely tenuous interstellar gas, the equally tenuous dust clouds and the radiation which traverses it in all directions) with here and there a (relatively) tiny speck of extremely hot, glowing matter. One at least of these specks has a number of still tinier specks of cold matter circling round it, and one of these is our home.

We have to say 'one at least' because at present we do not know whether any of the other stars possesses a family of planets like the sun's.

If Proxima Centauri had a planet revolving round it in an

orbit the diameter of Jupiter's, it would never appear further from the star than 4″. This angular distance, of course, is quite large – two stars 4″ apart can be seen separated distinctly in a very small telescope. But the planet is not emitting light of its own; it is shining merely by reflected light and its luminosity would be far less than that of a star of the same size. Moreover, when at maximum elongation, only one half of it would be lit up by the star and its brightness would be reduced very considerably in consequence.

The difference in brightness between a self-luminous body and one which is merely shining by reflected light is made clear by the sun and the moon. They are almost exactly the same apparent size, but sunlight is 1,000,000 times as bright as moonlight at full moon. If the moon were as far from the sun as Jupiter is it would be receiving only one twenty-seventh of the light that falls upon it where it actually is.

Even if the hypothetical planet were the same diameter as Proxima Centauri itself, therefore, it would be only $\frac{1}{27,000,000}$ as bright, and it would be lost in the glare of the star, however powerful the telescope.

It is true that the moon is made of very dark material, but even if our huge imaginary planet were made of material as white as snow it would still be invisible.

A planet as large as the star round which it revolves is an impossibility. If this planet were one tenth the diameter of Proxima, which is a reasonable proportion (Jupiter being about one tenth the diameter of the sun), the fraction quoted above would be $\frac{1}{4,700,000,000}$.

It is clear, therefore, that if there are planets accompanying more remote stars they would be quite invisible from the earth.

There is, however, a possibility that the presence of a massive planet might become evident indirectly. The moon causes the earth to revolve in an orbit of small diameter, and a very massive planet might do the same to the star round which it revolves.

In the early part of last century it was noticed that Sirius (the Dog Star – the brightest star in the sky) was moving in a closed elliptical path, and this was taken as evidence that it was accompanied by a massive planet. In 1862, however, an American optician, Alvan Clark, testing a telescope that he had just completed, detected a faint star close to Sirius; and after it had been observed for some time it became clear that this faint star was the cause of the orbital motion of Sirius – the two stars were revolving round one another in a period of about fifty years.

The fact that this companion of Sirius is a star and not a planet was established by its spectrum, which is quite unlike that of Sirius. If its light were merely that of Sirius reflected from its surface, its spectrum would be the same or nearly the same as that of Sirius.

This particular star is exceptionally interesting for another reason. It must be massive to cause Sirius itself to move appreciably, and yet its light is much fainter than that of Sirius. At first sight there seems nothing strange in that – the companion may be faint merely because it is at a low temperature. Its spectrum, however, is that of a star at an extremely high temperature. Its surface therefore must be very bright. Why then, if it is a massive star at a very high temperature, does it look so faint compared with Sirius? The only possible answer is that it must be very small; but then its density must be very high – impossibly high, as was thought at one time. Astronomers, in fact, preferred not to think about the companion to Sirius; it is uncomfortable to dwell upon a fact which is impossible.

The solution to this puzzle was comparatively simple. Atoms, as Rutherford proved, are something like miniature solar systems, consisting of an extremely tiny but relatively heavy nucleus and a number of very much lighter electrons which may be thought of as still tinier planets revolving in orbits round the nucleus.

Now in ordinary material objects such as ourselves, pieces of wood, lead, brick and so forth, all the electrons are present and the effective size of each atom is the diameter of the outermost electron 'orbit'. Two similar atoms in the normal state cannot come closer together than a distance equal to the diameter of those 'orbits'.

At high temperatures, however, some of the electrons become detached and wander about freely. The higher the temperature the more electrons become detached, until finally none remain – the nuclei are bare and unprotected.

In a high-temperature star, therefore, the atoms are capable of coming much closer together than they can at low temperatures. Under certain conditions this can actually happen; the star collapses, the 'shrunken' atoms come much closer together than they can when in the normal state, and therefore the material of the star becomes extremely dense – far denser than lead, or even gold.

The companion to Sirius is in this collapsed condition and it was the first star of its kind to be recognised. Such stars are known as 'white dwarfs'. As was mentioned earlier, a star of this type may be little larger than the earth but as heavy as the sun.

The alert reader will have been wondering why atoms, if they are like solar systems, cannot pack themselves together flatwise, like coins piled one on top of another. This does not happen, and that is one of the many reasons why physicists do not believe that electrons are really little particles revolving in planetary orbits; but to go into this fully would take us much too far from our theme, as would also an account of how the companion to Sirius has provided one of the crucial tests of Einstein's general theory of relativity.

We have been deflected from our course by this extremely interesting object. It was mentioned in the first place as a body that might have been a planet but which turned out to be a star – and a very odd star indeed. Within the last few years other stars have been suspected of being swung round in orbits by companions which have not yet been seen. These unseen bodies may be planets; on the other hand they may be white dwarfs too distant from us, or too close to their larger companions, to be seen.

The reason why astronomers are reluctant to assume the existence of other planetary systems is that so far they have been quite unable to account for the existence of the solar system of planets. There is at present no really satisfactory theory of how this system came into existence. The most satisfactory (or the least unsatisfactory) theories all presuppose a catastrophic origin – the collision, or very close approach, of two stars or some such event. The chance of the occurrence of any such event in any reasonable interval of time is extremely small. If, therefore, planetary systems can come into existence only as a result of some such event, then there cannot be many stars accompanied by planets. If, on the other hand, some plausible theory, not requiring an extremely unlikely catastrophe, could be formulated to account for the sun's retinue of planets, then we could say that there is a probability that a large proportion of the stars have planets.

There the matter must rest, In our account of the constitution of the galactic system we must perforce be vague about planets. We cannot see any (except those that accompany the sun) and we have no clues.

The galactic system is constructed on a vast and lavish scale. Our conception of it has been formed as a result of measurements of distances made by the methods described herein. If the validity of these methods is acknowledged, the picture of our system of stars, outlined very briefly in this chapter, must be accepted. To some people, no doubt, the picture will be unattractive, but that is no reason for rejecting it. Facts must be accepted and acknowledged, and our ways of thinking must be adjusted and adapted to them. If any reader is repelled by the thought of the utter insignificance of our planet in the galactic system, he may console himself by reflecting that his value in the scheme of things is not a matter of mere size. Another may be impressed by the aloofness of the stars – the feeling that they have nothing to do with him whatever; that if there is any purpose or plan in the galactic system it concerns him not at all. Such readers may perhaps be consoled by the thought that humility is counted as a virtue in most systems of morality.

There is an expressive American idiom for the puncturing of an inflated ego; its possessor is said to have been cut down to size. This process of cutting down to size has only just begun; we shall feel a great deal smaller before this survey is completed.

CHAPTER VIII

THE 'WHITE' NEBULÆ

At the end of Chapter 1, mention was made of a little wisp of misty light close to the margin of the Galaxy, easily visible without telescopic aid. This is the Great Nebula, known also as M 31 (or NGC 224), in the constellation of Andromeda. It is the most conspicuous member of a class of nebulæ which has been recognised for a very long time as distinct from those mentioned in Chapter 7. Their light is white instead of greenish and they are mostly regular in shape instead of wispy and irregular.

The spectroscope, in the hands of Huggins, revealed a further difference; the spectra of the green nebulæ were found to consist only of a few bright lines (as has already been mentioned), whereas those of the 'white' nebulæ were continuous bands of colours like the spectrum of a white-hot body. Later, with more powerful instruments, their spectra were found to be crossed by many dark absorption lines – in fact they strongly resemble the spectrum of the sun.

These white nebulæ were the subject of much controversy for many years. According to one view they were within the galactic system and members of it, the other view being that they were outside the galactic system altogether. Some daring speculators even suggested that they were systems of stars like the galactic system.

The most cogent argument in favour of the first view was based on the fact that their distribution seemed to be related systematically to the plane of the galaxy. It will be clear that in general the numbers of any class of objects within the galactic system that we may expect to find in equal areas of sky will be greatest along the galaxy itself and least in the directions of the poles of the galaxy, at right angles to its plane. This is true of stars, green nebulæ and obscuring clouds. The white nebulæ, on the contrary, were found to be least in number along the galaxy and greatest in number in regions away from it. This fact certainly proves that they are not distributed uniformly throughout the system, but it also seems to show that they are closely related to it. It was argued that if they were wholly external, and very remote, they would not pay any attention, as it were, to the galaxy but would be found roughly equally scattered over all parts of the sky.

This argument lost its force when the full extent of the obscuring dust clouds had been revealed. It could then be assumed that these nebulæ are indeed external, remote and (on the average) uniformly distributed, and that we do not see all those that are in the region of the galaxy because they are hidden by the obscuring clouds. It may be pointed out as an analogy that we see fewer stars near the horizon than we do overhead because they are obscured by the greater thickness of atmosphere, and the dust and haze in its lower layers, through which their light is trying to pass.

These white nebulæ are very faint objects and not much can be seen of their structure even in large telescopes. The Great nebula, M 31, is seen as an elongated, oval patch of faint, misty light, brightest at the centre (where there is a small, almost starlike nucleus) and fading gradually in all directions. At one side there is a dark rift running parallel to the length of the nebula. A little way away there are two other nebulæ, much smaller and fainter, which look as if they might be satellites.

Definite structure was seen in two of the smaller white nebulæ by the Earl of Rosse about ninety years ago with the aid of the reflecting telescope, six feet in diameter, made by him. This telescope collected nearly twice as much light as Herschel's four-foot telescope and was by far the largest telescope in existence in its day. It was only after more than half a century had elapsed that another telescope of the same size was made.

The structure revealed in these two nebulæ was startling; they were spiral in form, rather like catherine wheels. This was very different from the unorganised shapelessness of the majority of the green nebulæ, and the discovery sharpened the distinction between the two types.

No further progress was made until the application of photography to astronomy. Isaac Roberts, an English amateur astronomer, using a twenty-inch reflecting telescope in the nineties of last century, photographed a great many nebulæ. His photographs revealed that a high proportion of the white nebulæ are spiral in structure, including the most conspicuous of them – M 31 in Andromeda, shown in Plates V and VI. They are set at all angles to the line of sight, some broadside-on like the two that Lord Rosse had seen as spiral, some edge-on, others obliquely inclined like M 31. Many of those seen edge-on have a dark streak running symmetrically across them from side to side as in Plate VII. Others, not quite edge-on, show a dark streak which is clearly a belt of dark material encircling the nebula – Plate VIII. The 'rift' in M 31, visible to the eye in telescopes, was revealed as of the same character; but in this nebula the photographs showed not one but many dark bands.

The reason why photography reveals so much that the eye cannot see is this. However long we look at a thing, it does not look any brighter – as we all know. The emulsion on a photographic plate, however, is affected more the longer it is exposed. Every photographer knows this; he can get a well-exposed negative in dull weather simply by setting the shutter for a longer exposure time than would be necessary on a bright day. These very faint nebulæ, too dim to enable their true structure to be seen, impress their images strongly on the photographic emulsion if given enough time. An exposure of one hour on a fast plate, with a telescope having a focal length five times its diameter, is enough to give an image of M 31 in which very dim outlying parts, too faint to be seen at all in any telescope, are clearly represented – while the central part is seriously over-exposed.

That, incidentally, is one of the difficulties in photographing nebulæ; no single photograph can possibly represent the whole of a nebula correctly. A negative exposed for a short time, showing the small bright nucleus in M 31, does not reveal any

of the faint outer parts of the nebula. A longer exposure, sufficient to show these outer parts and their structure, mis-repre-
sents the central part, which appears on the negative as a large,
dense black patch in which the small nucleus is completely
lost. Plate VI, not so fully exposed as Plate V, shows more of
the structure of the central part of the nebula.

The revelation by photography of the structure of the white
nebulæ led to a revival of the view that they are systems of
stars, generally similar to the galactic system. Opinion was
divided as to their size. Before definite evidence was available
it was not easy to imagine that they were comparable in size
to the galactic system, for that would imply that this system,
so overwhelming in its vastness, is merely one of a very large
number of white nebulæ.

Another remarkable fact about these objects was revealed
by the spectroscope in the hands of V. M. Slipher, working at
the Flagstaff observatory in Arizona. Slipher photographed
the spectra of several nebulæ and compared the positions of
the lines in the spectra with those of lines produced by terrestrial substances. He found very large displacements of the
nebular lines, corresponding to sightline velocities very much
higher than any found among the galactic stars. M 31 was
found to be approaching the sun at 190 miles per second, but
a large part of this is accounted for by the sun's orbital motion
in the galactic system. Others were receding with very great
speeds, up to 1125 miles per second. These results were obtained in the period 1912 to 1925.

No such velocities are found among any of the objects in
the galactic system. The discovery of these very high velocities
made it impossible any longer to maintain the view that these
nebulæ are members of the galactic system.

As time went on more sightline velocities were measured
and it became clear that all but a very few of the nebulæ were
receding from us. Perhaps, however, it would be safer merely
to say that the line-displacements in their spectra were, with
very few exceptions, towards the red end of the spectrum.
Caution is necessary for a reason that will appear later.

The establishment of the fact that some, at least, of the white nebulæ are stellar systems comparable with the galactic system required larger telescopes than that used by Slipher, the diameter of which was two feet. The work was undertaken by the Mount Wilson observatory, in California, which is equipped with two reflecting telescopes, one of five feet diameter (Plate XIV) and the other of eight feet four inches – one hundred inches (Plate XV). This latter was, and still is, the largest telescope in the world in actual use. It is always referred to as the hundred-inch, its smaller companion being known as the sixty-inch.

With these telescopes, large-scale photographs of M 31 and other nebulæ were taken at frequent intervals. Close study of the photographs of M 31, larger and better defined than any that had hitherto been obtained, showed that the faint, misty light of its outer parts was due to multitudes of stars. All these stars, of course, are the same distance from us, within one or two per cent. It is possible to obtain spectra of the brighter of these stars, but the majority are much too faint. It is possible, however, to determine their colours, and therefore their spectral type. This is done by taking photographs with plates sensitive to blue light only and others with plates sensitive to red light as well as blue. Obviously low-temperature stars, which are reddish, will show more prominently on the red-sensitive plates than on those sensitive to blue only. Equally obviously very hot stars (the B-type stars) will show relatively more prominently on the blue-sensitive plates than on those sensitive to red as well.

This method of determining the colours of stars had been in use for a long time for stars in the galactic system, and the relation between colour and spectral type had been established. By applying the same method to the stars in M 31 their spectral types could be determined. It was, however, necessary to correct the results for the effect of reddening of the light by absorption in the dust clouds of the galactic system.

By comparing photographs taken at different times, variable stars were discovered and their periods determined. Among these variable stars are many cepheids, and it was found that they show the same relationship between their absolute magnitudes and their periods as do those in the Magellanic Clouds and in the globular clusters, as well as those scattered throughout the galactic system.

The photographs also showed clusters of various types including globular clusters, and dark obscuring clouds.

It has been mentioned earlier that features of uniformity have been discovered among the stars of the galactic system, for example the high intrinsic luminosity of the B-type stars and of the cepheids of long period. It was found that these features of uniformity are present also in the stars of M 31. For example, the bluish-white stars are among the brightest, as are also the long-period cepheids.

In short, nearly every type of object known in the galactic system was found also in M 31. All these objects being at the same distance from us, the various features of uniformity showed up at once.

When this exploration of the contents of M 31 had been completed, it was possible to determine its distance by several independent methods; by the cepheid relationship, the average magnitudes of stars of different spectral types (the B-type stars being especially useful), and by the magnitudes of novæ.

These last-mentioned objects have been mentioned only once before, and some further explanation of their nature is necessary. 'Nova' is the astronomer's name for what is popularly known as a new star. From time to time a bright star suddenly appears where no star had been seen before. The word 'suddenly' is appropriate, because it usually takes only a few hours to reach its maximum brightness. It does not remain bright for very long – it begins to fade very soon and after some months it usually becomes inconspicuous.

The reason why the term 'new star' is inappropriate is that invariably a faint star in the position of the 'new' one is found on photographs of the region taken some time previously. What has happened is not the sudden creation of a star from nothing, but the sudden increase of luminosity, by a thousand-fold or more, of an already existing star.

These novæ occur at fairly frequent intervals in the galactic system and an approximate idea has been obtained of their intrinsic luminosity at maximum. Entirely similar objects were found in M 31, and their magnitude at maximum, relative to the magnitudes of stars of known types, indicated that in general their intrinsic luminosities, or absolute magnitudes, are of the same order as those occurring in the galactic system.

All these various criteria agreed in assigning a distance of 210,000 parsecs (680,000 light-years) to this nebula. Its diameter proved to be little, if any, smaller than that of the galactic system.

Similar surveys were made of the contents of another conspicuous spiral nebula, M 33 (or NGC 598), in the constellation of Triangulum (Plate XVIII). This does not look so large as M 31 and is actually smaller, because its distance is only very slightly, if at all, greater than that of M 31. It is nearly broadside on to the line of sight.

M 33 also contains stars of familiar types, including cepheids, as well as clusters, gaseous nebulæ and obscuring clouds. The central part of M 31 cannot be 'resolved' into separate stars, but that of M 33 can be seen to consist of stars, distributed very much as they are in its outer parts.

So far as can be judged, the galactic system resembles M 33 rather than M 31. Among other things, the relative abundance of stars of different types in M 33 is more like that found in the galactic system than in M 31. If there is a planet in M 33 inhabited by beings like ourselves, they would be able to see the galactic system with the naked eye, as we see the Great Nebula M 31. On photographs it would look rather like our photographs of M 33, but larger: It would not appear broadside-on, but tilted or inclined, though not so much as M 31 does to us. We cannot be certain at present that the galactic system is spiral in structure, but it probably is.

As the distance between M 31 and M 33 is only about 65,000 parsecs (200,000 light-years) either of them would be very conspicuous in the sky of any planet situated in the other – three and one half times as large as they appear to us.

Not all the white nebulæ are spiral in structure, nor even circular. The two Magellanic Clouds (Plates IX and X), which were first investigated by Miss Leavitt, are examples of completely irregular nebulæ, having no symmetry whatever. They are much closer to us than are M 31 and M 33. The distance of the Greater Magellanic Cloud from the sun is about 26,000 parsecs (85,000 light-years) while that of the Lesser Magellanic Cloud is about 30,000 parsecs (98,000 light-years). They are very much smaller than M 31 and M 33, and they have somewhat the same relationship to the galactic system as the two small nebulæ near M 31, already mentioned, have to that system; but they are of a totally different type.

There are two other systems, both irregular, the distances of which are comparable with those of M 31 and M 33. Three others, which are heavily obscured by the dust clouds of the galaxy, may also be at similar distances, as judged by their apparent size; but owing to the fact that they are obscured and dimmed to an unknown extent, the methods which were used with success for estimating the distances of M 31 and M 33 could not be applied to them.

To anticipate a little, the distances between these ten systems are very much smaller than the average, and they therefore constitute a group or cluster. They appear to be moving relatively to one another, but at velocities which are comparatively small – not much greater than the velocities of some stars in the galactic system.

There may be other members of this local group or cluster, hidden by the dust-clouds of the galaxy. Some of these clouds (particularly those which lie in the direction of the centre of the galactic system) are completely opaque and at present there is no way of finding out what lies beyond them. Within the last few years, however, a discovery has been made which may in time afford a means of penetrating these barriers. It has been found that not only the sun, but the galaxy, is emitting radiation of very low frequency and long wave-length which can be detected by suitable wireless receivers. At present the receiving apparatus is not sufficiently 'directional'; it cannot discriminate between different parts of the sky less than a few degrees apart. In time, however, as technical advances are made, the apparatus will doubtless be improved in this respect and may provide us with a new means of exploring the universe.

Already the radar equipment used during the war for detecting aircraft, flying bombs and rockets has been used effectively for observing meteors and has provided yet another method (though not a very accurate one) for measuring the distance of the moon. Radar has its limitations in astronomy, however. We have to wait only about three seconds to get the distance of the moon, that being the time taken for the signal or pulse to travel to the moon and back. If it were possible to use the same method on M 31, we should have to wait 1,360,000 years or so.

CHAPTER IX

EXPLORING THE DEPTHS OF SPACE

THE two large telescopes on Mount Wilson, California, were employed in a systematic survey of the sky, similar to that undertaken by Herschel over a century earlier, but with two differences; it was a photographic survey, and it ignored the galactic system entirely except in so far as the obscuring effect of the dust clouds in that system had to be taken into account.

This survey showed that the total number of these external systems of stars within reach of the telescopes was enormous. They were found to cluster thickly in some parts of the sky and to be more thinly scattered in others, but they are present everywhere except in the zone occupied by the galaxy. Even there, a few were found showing through gaps in the dust clouds, much as stars show through gaps in terrestrial clouds. They are of all apparent sizes, from M 31, which extends over about 2° (very faint extensions bring this up to nearly 4°) to minute objects the images of which are scarcely to be distinguished from those of faint stars. They are also of widely different shapes, from complex spiral structures like M 31 or M 33 to round, structureless blobs. Some of the spirals have two arms only, some have many. Some have arms which extend only a small fraction of the complete circumference, in others the arms are wrapped two or three times round the central portions. There is a class, known as the 'barred spirals', in which the central portion has two straight arms projecting from it in opposite directions, and spiral arms springing from the tips of these arms. In some examples of this class these arms do not 'spiral' appreciably, but are more nearly like the rim of a wheel, giving such nebulæ something of the appearance of the Greek letter Θ – see Plate XII. Others are like the letter S.

Away from the Galaxy nebulæ are found in great numbers. On some of the negatives there are as many nebula images as there are images of stars of the galactic system, and the total number within reach of the 100-inch is enormous – one hundred million or more.

They are not by any means scattered uniformly over the sky (apart from the obscuration along the galaxy) and in fact clusters of nebulæ are common. Some such clusters comprise only a dozen or so nebulæ, while others include hundreds. In some of these clusters the apparent distances between the nebulæ are surprisingly small – very much smaller, relative to the size of the individual members, than they are in our local cluster. Indeed, some of the photographs (for example Plate XIII) show images which are almost in contact, although this may be misleading; the nebulæ may be separated by a considerable distance in the line of sight. Even after due allowance is made for this, however, the crowding together in certain of the clusters is very striking.

It will have been noticed that these objects are now being called simply nebulæ, without qualification. Originally this name was given to all misty patches or wisps of faint light in the sky, but when the true nature of the 'white' nebulæ was confirmed there was considerable discussion about the most suitable name for them. They are outside the galactic system and can therefore be described as 'extra-galactic nebulæ', but that is cumbersome. They are comparable with the galactic system, which was thought at one time to comprise the whole universe, and the name 'island universes' was therefore suggested. This, however, is open to the serious objection that the universe is the whole totality of things, and has no plural. If we call every system of stars a universe, we have no name left for the universe itself, which includes them all.

They are also often referred to as 'galaxies', but this also is open to objection. The word 'galaxy' properly means the Milky Way. It has no plural. Our system of stars is described as the galactic system; but that is its proper name, in the same sense that London is the proper name for the large city on the

Thames. To describe these objects as 'milky ways' is not at all apt, while to refer to them as 'galactic systems' is as unjustifiable as it would be to refer to all very large cities as 'Londons'.

It seems fitting, therefore, to apply to them the generic term 'nebula', and to differentiate the relatively minute glowing clouds of gas in the galactic system (and other similar systems) by referring to them as 'gaseous nebulæ'. It might be better to devise some quite different name for these objects.

The clusters are useful in the same way that the Lesser Magellanic Cloud was useful; we know that all the objects in it are at substantially the same distance from us and that in consequence their actual sizes are proportional to their apparent sizes. Their actual luminosities also are proportional to their apparent luminosities. It is true that a cluster might possibly be very much larger in the line of sight than at right angles to it, but that could scarcely be true of all of them. It is also true that a few objects apparently in the cluster might be 'field' objects – objects very much nearer or very much further away than the cluster – but these few could not affect the conclusion appreciably.

The conclusion from inspection of photographs of nebula clusters is that the nebulæ do not differ very much in actual total brightness. This is a most important fact, because what is true of nebulæ in clusters is probably (almost certainly) true of all nebulæ. We can therefore assume that, in general, the distances of nebulæ are roughly inversely proportional to their apparent brightness.

It was pointed out earlier that this is true, in a very general sense, of the stars in the galactic system. The stars, however, differ among themselves in real or intrinsic luminosity (and also in size) very much more than do the nebulæ. If we based our estimates of the distances of stars on the simple assumption that they are all equally bright, we should be making enormous errors in the case of individual stars, and even in the case of relatively large numbers of stars treated statistically. If we base our estimates of the relative distances of nebulæ on the same assumption, we shall not be making any serious errors in the statistical sense.

If we look more closely at the nebulæ in the clusters we find that the uniformity is still more marked when we take account of their type. The small ones are found to be structureless – globular or oval – and the large ones are usually fully-developed spirals, although a few are irregular like the Magellanic Clouds. Those of intermediate size are of intermediate types. This has enabled the various types to be arranged in an orderly sequence, corresponding to increasing size, which may have significance in connection with theories of the evolution of the nebulæ.

A very homely analogy is the close correspondence between the characteristics of human beings and their size. If we arrange various specimens in order of size, we find that the smallest are rather shapeless, with very big heads in relation to their bodies, while the largest are more shapely and have large bodies relative to their heads. The body-head ratio has intermediate values in the intermediate sizes. Other characteristics also would be found to progress, or at least to vary systematically, along the size sequence. For example, the number of teeth would increase rapidly to a steady maximum, and then decrease again rather more slowly. But we are all familiar with the characteristics of babies, toddlers, children, youths and maidens, men and women.

The analogy is surprisingly close in another respect. Among human beings the differentiation between the sexes is slight in the smallest specimens, but is very marked further along the size sequence. So it is with the nebulæ; among the larger specimens there are two well-differentiated types, the regular spirals like M 31 and M 33 and the 'barred' spirals. In the small, relatively shapeless specimens we cannot at present distinguish any 'sex' characteristics. (In Plate XIII there is one specimen of each of these types and a 'freak' which seems to have taken a corkscrew for a pattern.)

We must be on our guard, however; the above analogy should not be pressed too far. We must not assume that the small, structureless nebulæ will grow into big spirals, or that the big spirals have developed from structureless ones. It seems very likely that this is the order of things, but there is no proof.

Another thing that must be pointed out is that the sizes and intrinsic luminosities of nebulæ of any one type are nothing like so uniform as the sizes of human beings of the same age. The 'scatter' or spread is considerable and it is the averages that display the systematic relations explained above. Even in our local cluster this can be seen ; M 33 belongs to a class or type which on the average is larger than the class or type to which M 31 belongs, but it is only about half the diameter of M 31. Analogically, M 33 is a stunted adult and M 31 is a strapping, six-foot-six youth. The galactic system seems to be about average for its type.

While we are discussing clusters, another of their characteristics should be mentioned. All the clusters which include four or five hundred nebulæ are remarkably alike except in apparent size. If we take photographs of all of them and enlarge those of the apparently smaller ones to the same scale as that of the apparently largest, the uniformity is very striking; the overwhelming impression is that the differences of apparent size are simply due to differences of distance. We shall see later that this impression is amply confirmed.

At this stage, then, we are in the position of knowing the distances of a few relatively near nebulæ with considerable accuracy, these distances having been found by applying methods and criteria already used with success throughout the galactic system. Beyond these near nebulæ, members of a small local cluster, there are millions of others, presumably much more remote, which have been surveyed by taking representative samples. The survey has yielded several features of uniformity which enable us to place the nebulæ roughly in order of distance. The clusters, moreover, can be arranged in order of distance with considerable accuracy, if we make the assumption that apparent uniformity throughout the members of the various clusters implies real uniformity. The gap between the local cluster and the rest of the nebulæ, however, remains to be bridged before we can step out with confidence into the far distances.

The first step is to see if any of the nebulæ, other than those of the local cluster, contain any stars or other objects similar to those with which we are familiar in the galactic system, and in particular cepheids. Unfortunately the largest telescope in use – the 100-inch – is not large enough to reveal cepheids with certainty in any of these more remote systems. It does, however, show novæ, very bright B-type stars and other identifiable objects in a few of them. These, therefore, can have distances assigned to them which, though more uncertain than those assigned to M 31 and M 33, are nevertheless of the right order of magnitude. Beyond these, there are nebulæ in which only a very few stars can be distinguished. All that can be done is to compare these stars with the very brightest stars in the galactic system and in nebulæ of the local cluster. This comparison can be relied on with some confidence because there are good reasons for believing that no star (apart from novæ) can be more than about 50,000 times as bright as the sun. In any system consisting of many millions of stars, we can be confident that a few will attain or closely approach this maximum.

Novæ have already been mentioned in this connection. These occur fairly frequently in the galactic system and in its near neighbours M 31 and M 33, roughly at the rate of twenty to fifty per year. There is another type of nova, very much more rare, which attains a brightness at maximum many thousands of times greater than normal novæ. One such may be expected to appear about every five hundred years in any one nebula. There was one in the galactic system in 1572 which was visible in daylight and another in M 31 (in 1885) the brightness of which was a large fraction of the total brightness of the nebula. Others have been seen in other nebulæ from time to time.

These supernovæ are useful because, being so very much brighter than any other stars, they are visible when they appear in very distant nebulæ, and enable an estimate to be made of their distance as a check on other methods. It has to be assumed that all supernovæ everywhere have the same intrinsic brightness, and this may be only approximately true. However, a careful watch is kept for 'new' stars in nebulæ which are of such a small apparent size that normal stars within it cannot be expected to be distinguishable.

Fortunately, the nearest of the large clusters (in the constellation Virgo) contains well-developed spirals in which a few stars can be distinguished, and these have enabled a fairly reliable distance to be assigned to the cluster – rather more than two million parsecs, or about seven million light-years. This at once gives the distances of all the other large clusters to the same order of accuracy, on the assumption mentioned above.

As the investigation proceeds we can check the results by making use of the features of uniformity which were derived from the clusters by comparing the nebulæ within it one with another. The checks reveal a self-consistent whole; they confirm one another and leave no doubt that we are on the right road. Many have collaborated in finding this road. Among them the names of Hubble, Humason and Slipher will always be remembered.

THE RED-SHIFTS

It was mentioned earlier that Slipher found displacements of spectrum lines towards the red or low-frequency end of the spectrum corresponding to velocities of recession of some of the nebulæ up to 1125 miles per second. These results were published in 1925. It was not long before the 100-inch, in the hands of Humason, revealed still greater displacements. At first, only nebulæ in clusters were examined, as it was important to find out whether there was any systematic relation between the amount of the displacement or shift and the distance of the nebula. As already explained, the relative distances of the clusters were known, on a reasonable assumption, and the distances of some of them were presumably very large indeed. Therefore they would show any systematic relation, if it existed, with little or no uncertainty.

The first result was a red-shift, for one of the (apparently) larger clusters, corresponding to a velocity of recession of 2400 miles per second. Other results quickly followed for progressively smaller and fainter clusters, and when the limit of the capacity of the 100-inch had been reached, a red-shift corresponding to a velocity of recession of 26,000 miles per second had been recorded. This is about one seventh of the velocity of light.

The amount of the red-shift (expressed as velocity) was found to be in simple proportion to the relative distance of the cluster. This is the simplest possible relation and can be expressed in the simplest language – the more distant the cluster, the greater the red-shift. Moreover, if the red-shift is taken to be the Döppler effect, due to motion in the line of sight, then the more distant the cluster, the faster it is receding from us.

In dealing with objects in the galactic system we have never hesitated to interpret displacements of the spectrum lines as due to motion in the line of sight, and the consistency of the results has amply borne out this confidence. But in these cases the displacement is small; it needs a low-power microscope to detect and an elaborate, accurately-constructed machine to measure.

The displacements or shifts seen in the spectra of the nebulæ are altogether different in amount; they can be seen by the naked eye without the slightest difficulty. The nebulæ which show these large shifts are small and faint, and the only absorption lines which can be made out are those due to calcium. There are two of them, known as the H and K lines, and they are at the extreme violet end of the spectrum. This region of the spectrum, although it can be photographed easily, is almost invisible to the eye; young people can distinguish the H and K lines in the sun's spectrum, but those past middle age cannot.

In the spectrum of nebulæ in a cluster in Ursa Major (the Great Bear or Plough) these lines are shifted well into the middle of the blue region. This is something entirely unprecedented; it is a conspicuous change of colour. Lines normally in the green part of the spectrum, if they could be distinguished, would appear in the red part.

As more and more spectra were obtained and measured, it was found that everywhere the same rule held – if the criteria explained above showed that a nebula was very distant, then the red-shift (the displacement of the calcium lines towards the red end of its spectrum) was large. Once this had been established for a sufficient number of nebulæ (the clusters playing a decisive part) the red-shift could be used as a gauge for all nebulæ.

The principle is the same as that underlying the many methods explained earlier. Once a feature of uniformity has been found among objects the distances of which are already known, it can be applied to objects of unknown distances. The validity of this extension from the known to the unknown is established by its success – by the self-consistency of the results. The cepheid relationship enabled us to step out boldly beyond the limits of stellar parallax measurements and the results have amply justified this boldness. So it is with the red-shifts in the spectra of the nebulæ; wherever this criterion of distance is applied, it fits in with the other criteria, each supporting and confirming the others.

We can now take a comprehensive look at this universe, as revealed by the 100-inch telescope. Within a sphere the radius of which is about one hundred and fifty million parsecs, or five hundred million light-years, there are roughly one hundred million nebulæ, one of which (and one of the largest) is our own system of stars, the galactic system. They are of many different types, but a nebula of any particular type in one part of this space can be matched in any other part of it. Perhaps this is the most striking feature of the universe – the uniformity to be found everywhere. We saw the same thing in the galactic system; everywhere the same types, repeated endlessly – stars like the sun as common as daisies in a field. Now we find the same thing in the universe at large. Not only are the nebulæ of the various types alike wherever they are found, but their constituents (in so far as present knowledge goes) are alike. If it is surprising to find stars like the sun by the million in the galactic system, it is still more so to find them so thickly scattered in these other systems that the spectra of most of them (due to the combined light of all the stars in them) are almost the same as that of the sun.

The nebulæ are scattered, on the whole, fairly uniformly throughout the space already explored, but they congregate in clusters, some large, some small. The clusters themselves seem to be uniformly distributed. The average spacing of the nebulæ is comparable with tennis balls fifty feet apart.

Up to the limits of distance reached by the 100-inch telescope no thinning-out can be detected with certainty. In all directions (apart from the obscuring region of the Galaxy) the numbers of nebulæ in equal areas of the sky are roughly equal. Averaged, there are about 2400 in each square degree. At any moment the moon is probably hiding nearly five hundred of them.

Above all, these nebulæ (except our companions of the local cluster) are all apparently receding from us and the further they are away the faster they are receding. Those at the limit of our present observing resources are (apparently) receding from us at a velocity about one seventh of that of light, corresponding to a distance of about 250,000,000 light-years. Nebulæ much more distant than this can be photographed, but at present their red-shifts cannot be directly measured.

A more cautious statement of this property of the universe is that in whatever direction we look we see nebulæ at various distances up to about 500,000,000 light-years and the light from these nebulæ is increased in wavelength (and diminished in frequency) when it reaches us, by an amount proportional to their distances from us.

It must now be said that if the red-shifts indicate motion, it is only a half-truth to say that all these millions of objects are receding from us. The other half of the truth is that we are receding from each of them. The whole truth is that they are receding from one another – spreading apart, in fact. The galactic system is no more the centre of the universe than the earth or the sun. It is merely one of a vast crowd. Observers on a planet in any one of the nebulæ would observe precisely what we observe; the red-shifts (including that in the spectrum of the galactic system) would be proportional to distances from him, and he would say (speaking half the truth) that the nebulæ, including this one in which *we* live, were receding from *him*.

It so often happens that half-truths conflict, and that the conflict is resolved when whole truths are substituted.

If the red-shifts are really due to motion in the line of sight some difficult questions arise. The most obvious is that the nebulæ would not now be where they appear to be. We see them by the light that they emitted a very long time ago. Even our two most conspicuous neighbours, M 31 and M 33, appear to us not as they are now, but as they were nearly three-quarters of a million years ago.

In passing, it can be shown that even the shape of a nebula may not be what it appears to be. M 31 is highly inclined, with the result that light by which we see its further edge left 40,000 years before light by which we see its nearer border. As it is rotating, it is clear that the further edge would have moved round somewhat by the time its light reached the nearer edge. In other words, as we see the nebula at any instant, the further edge is 40,000 years older than the nearer edge. It must therefore look distorted, but the amount of the distortion is unknown.

Returning to the nebulæ generally, it is clear that the further out we go, the greater is the discrepancy. At the limit of the 100 inch, the nebulæ are seen as and where they were 500,000,000 years ago. Now, if they are really receding, they are very much further away. This consideration raises the question (among others) of what we really mean by 'now'. The whole subject is of very great interest, but it is rather outside the scope of our theme.

There is another point which may be mentioned in passing. Presumably the nebulæ are changing or evolving progressively, possibly along the sequence of increasing size already mentioned. If so, the rate of change must be very slow because there is no obvious systematic difference of type between the nearer nebulæ and the more distant, which we see now as they were many millions of years ago.

The nebulæ, of course, have individual motions among themselves. These motions are much the same throughout the volume of space that can be observed. An interesting feature of the red-shift criterion of distance is that the greater the distance the greater the accuracy of its determination, reckoned as a percentage or fraction of the distance. The reason is that as the distance increases the effect of the individual motions on the red-shifts becomes a smaller and smaller fraction of the red-shift due to distance alone. The individual motion of a nebula may increase or diminish the observed shift, but in the case of a very distant nebula this effect is only a very small fraction of the shift.

Moreover, the value of the red-shifts as a criterion of distance is quite independent of any theories or speculations about its cause or significance. This must be qualified, however; if the shifts are due to some unknown cause other than motion in the line of sight, then we can say that the nebulæ are *now* where they were when the light left them, apart from the effects of their random individual motions among themselves. If they are simply the Döppler effect, then, as already pointed out, allowance must be made for the recession that has taken place since the light set out.

The spectroscope, as used in this investigation, may be compared to a radar receiver. The operator knows that the distance between the zero point on the screen and the 'blip' is proportional to the distance between the receiving aerial and the aircraft responsible for the 'blip'. He or she need not know anything about electronics or the properties of electromagnetic radiations; these subjects are of great interest, but from the operator's point of view they are irrelevant.

If astronomers were interested only in the distances of the nebulæ they could regard their spectra much as the radar operator regards the cathode-ray-tube screen, measure the red-shifts, work out the distances and leave it at that. Astronomers, however, are interested in everything to do with the universe. They want to know the cause and significance of the shifts. If they are due to motion in the line of sight they want to know the origin of the motion. In a later chapter we shall give some attention to this subject.

CHAPTER X

LARGE REFLECTING TELESCOPES

THE title of this book is *The Size of the Universe*. What is its size? It is at least one thousand million light-years in diameter. This figure might have been larger if the Californian town of Pasadena had not increased so greatly in size during the past thirty years. It would certainly have been much larger by now if there had been no war.

The lights of Los Angeles, which is quite near the 100-inch (or should we say that the 100-inch is quite near Los Angeles?) illuminate the night sky of Mount Wilson to such an extent that really long exposures cannot be made; the reflected light in the sky fogs the plates. For a similar reason (the lights of Greenwich and Blackheath) among others the Royal Observatory is being removed to Hurstmonceux in Sussex.

The observatory on Mount Wilson will not be moved, but a new one is being established some hundred miles further south-east, away from city lights, on Mount Palomar. This will have a telescope of 200 inches aperture, and a number of other smaller ones. The 200-inch will collect four times as much light as the 100-inch, and will therefore double the radius of the sphere within which nebulæ can be observed. If there are nebulæ one thousand million light-years away, the 200-inch will detect them and photograph their spectra. We shall then know whether the relation of simple proportionality between distance (as judged by apparent luminosity) and red-shift (expressed as velocity of recession) still holds at such distances. If so, we may expect to find the H and K lines in the green part of the spectrum instead of in the extreme violet, a shift corresponding to a velocity nearly one third of that of light. We may expect also to know whether the nebulæ thin out in these more remote regions, or whether their average spacing remains the same throughout this vast space, eight times greater in volume than that available to the 100-inch. In that case, the answer to our question will have to be 'at least two thousand million light-years in diameter'.

The 200-inch can also be expected to reveal more stars in the less remote nebulæ and to enable their types to be recognised. If cepheids can be detected in only a few of the nebulæ beyond the local cluster it will enable their distances to be determined with great accuracy, and this gain in accuracy will enable the scale of the whole system of nebulæ to be adjusted and improved. In fact the work already done with the 100-inch is only in the nature of a preliminary survey and the bulk of the work remains to be done with the larger telescope. When the limit of the 200-inch has been reached, exploration of the universe must cease until a larger telescope even than the 'giant of Mount Palomar' can be made.

This great telescope would almost certainly have been in use some years ago, and we should have had the answers to some of these questions by now, if there had been no war. At the beginning of the war the great observatory building with its rotating dome and the mounting for the 200-inch mirror had been completed and work was proceeding on the mirror itself at Pasadena. This work was suspended when the United States became involved in the war and was resumed at the end of 1945. The mirror was finished in the latter part of 1947 and the telescope is expected to be in use some time in 1948.

The surface of this huge mirror, over seventeen feet in diameter, must be perfectly polished and of parabolic curvature, so accurate in shape that no part of it is in error by more than two millionths of an inch. Such a thing cannot be done in a day; the work must proceed very slowly and cautiously. Haste is fatal – a few minutes' rashness may set the work back a month or more.

We can picture this accuracy by imagining a scale model, just as we have done for the solar system, but this model differs from most in that it is immensely larger than the original. The radius of curvature of the 200-inch mirror is 1335 inches. In our model the radius of curvature is 3950 *miles*. The central part of the curved surface of the 'model' mirror will just fit the earth's surface and its diameter will be 592 miles. The depth of the concavity of the real mirror is 3¾ inches. In the model it is just over 11 miles.

To match the real mirror, the surface of this 592-mile mirror

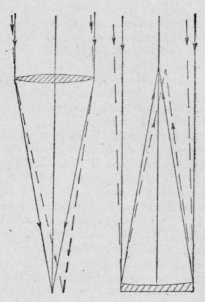

FIGURE 31

must not depart anywhere from the true parabolic shape by more than one third of an inch.

We have mentioned reflecting telescopes from time to time but have not hitherto described them, nor explained why they are used in preference to refracting telescopes for these investigations.

The formation of an image by a lens is familiar to everyone, but it is not so generally known that a concave mirror also forms an image. Figure 31 shows a lens and a mirror side by side, each receiving a parallel beam of light from a star. The lens bends the rays inwards by refraction in the glass and they all come to a focus at a single point. A single lens such as is shown in the diagram cannot bring the rays accurately to a point; there must be at least two differently-shaped lenses made of different kinds of glass, but we need not go too deeply into technical details. The mirror, if it is parabolic and not spherical, 'bends' the rays inwards by reflection at its surface and brings them all to a focus at a single point.

A lens builds up an image of a face, a landscape or a nebula point by point. Each point on the object sends a beam of light, like that shown in the diagram, on to the lens, which refracts it to form a point image. The image is simply the sum of all these point images.

A mirror does exactly the same thing; but the image is in front of the mirror, and if we try to look at it our head obstructs the light. This difficulty, of course, does not arise in the case of a lens, and it is no wonder that the first telescope was a refracting telescope, with a lens to form the image.

The problem of looking at the image formed by a mirror without obstructing the light was solved in three different ways by three men – Newton, an Englishman, Gregory, a Scotsman, and Cassegrain, a Frenchman. Figure 32 shows the three types of telescope.

In the Newtonian type a small flat mirror (or a right-angled prism) is supported in the middle of the tube near its upper end. This small mirror reflects the converging beam of light sideways through a hole in the side of the tube, where the image can be seen through an eyepiece.

In the Gregorian type a small concave mirror is used, which reflects the beam back through a hole in the main mirror. The light comes to a focus first, before striking the small mirror, and one result of this is that the final image formed behind the main mirror is erect, not inverted as in a refracting telescope. For this reason, Gregorian telescopes were used at one time as terrestrial telescopes or 'spy-glasses'.

In the Cassegrain type the small mirror is convex and, like the flat mirror of the Newtonian, it is placed so that the light from the main mirror strikes it before coming to a focus. The final image is therefore inverted, and telescopes of this type are therefore not suitable for terrestrial use.

The Gregorian and Cassegrain types have this in common,

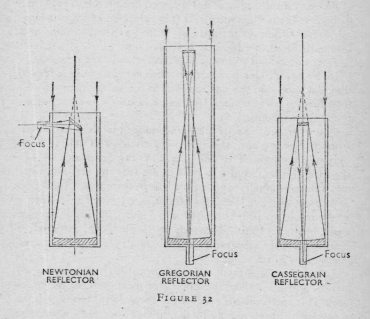

NEWTONIAN
REFLECTOR

GREGORIAN
REFLECTOR

CASSEGRAIN
REFLECTOR

FIGURE 32

that the final image is on a larger scale than it would be if the main mirror were used alone. The Cassegrain, however, is shorter than the Gregorian, other things being equal, and is therefore preferred for astronomical use. In very large telescopes this advantage is of great importance.

All three types of reflector suffer from loss of light due to obstruction by the small mirror. The loss is not so great as might appear from the diagrams, however. Even if the diameter of the small mirror is one third that of the main mirror only one ninth of the light is lost.

The mirrors of all the early reflecting telescopes were made of an alloy of copper and tin, known as speculum metal ('speculum' being Latin for mirror) and did not reflect a high proportion of the light. Since about the middle of last century, when a method was discovered of depositing a thin film of silver on glass, speculum metal has gone out of use and glass is universally used. Within the last few years a further improvement has been made; pure aluminium is used instead of silver. Aluminium has two great advantages; it does not tarnish as silver does and it reflects a much higher proportion of violet and ultra-violet, which are photographically more active than light of lower frequency.

When a reflecting telescope is used for photography it is possible to avoid a second reflection by placing the photographic plate at the principal focus, in a holder supported, like the small mirrors in Figure 32, in the middle of the tube near its upper end. This holder obstructs some of the light, as the small mirrors do, but the image is brighter than it is in any of the two-mirror arrangements because the light undergoes only one reflection.

There has always been a great deal of argument about the relative merits of refracting and reflecting telescopes. We need not concern ourselves with this controversy, which is largely pointless because both types have their uses; refractors are used for many purposes for which reflectors would be unsuitable, and *vice versa*. Reflectors, however, have one undisputed advantage over refractors – they can be made larger.

It is more difficult to make a large telescope of either type than it is to make a small one, but in the case of refractors the difficulty increases so rapidly with increasing size of the lens, or object-glass, that the largest successful object-glass ever made is only forty inches in diameter. It is always risky to make negative prophecies, but it is safe to say that it will be a very long time before a larger object-glass is made. It is doubtful whether it would be worth while to make it in any case.

There are a great many reflecting telescopes larger than this, and indeed a 40-inch reflector is regarded nowadays as quite a modest affair.

The 100-inch was completed in 1917. The main mirror was worked by G. W. Ritchey, and it took him six years to attain the perfect optical surface, accurate to two millionths of an inch. The mirror weighs five tons, and many difficult technical problems were involved in mounting it so that it can easily be pointed to any part of the sky within its reach, and driven accurately to follow the object being observed.

The 200-inch will be an improvement on the 100-inch in many respects, apart from its greater size. It will benefit from the experience gained, and the lessons learnt, in the construction of the 100-inch.

One very important improvement is that all parts of the sky visible at Mount Palomar will be accessible to the 200-inch. In designing the mounting for the 100-inch, stability and rigidity were rightly deemed to be the most important considerations, and this led to the adoption of a form of mounting which is immensely rigid and stable, but which prevents the telescope from being pointed to any part of the sky within about 34° of the North Pole. This disadvantage has been avoided very ingeniously in the mounting of the 200-inch, which will be able to explore these polar regions of the sky not accessible to the 100-inch.

Another important improvement is in the material of which the main mirror (and the secondary mirrors also) is composed. The 100-inch mirror is a solid slab of ordinary glass, such as windows are made of. This kind of glass has a relatively high coefficient of thermal expansion – that is to say, a rise or fall of temperature causes it to expand or contract to a considerable extent. All kinds of glass conduct heat very slowly, and the result is that when the mirror, warmed during the day, is exposed to the night sky, it cools rapidly on the outside, but the interior remains warm owing to the low conductivity of the glass. This unequal cooling alters the shape (or the 'figure', as opticians call it) of the reflecting surface and impairs the definition of the images formed by it. In fact the mirror performs really well only after it has been cooling for many hours. The best performance of all is obtained in exceptional weather conditions (most often in the autumn) when the temperature changes very little throughout the twenty-four hours.

The mirrors of the 200-inch are made of a different kind of glass, similar to that from which heat-resisting glass ovenware is made, the coefficient of expansion of which is only one quarter of that of ordinary glass. In addition, the main mirror is not a mere slab of glass, but is moulded at the back with numerous deep cavities, somewhat like a honeycomb. Thus the glass is nowhere more than a few inches thick, and consequently the mirror can cool down to a uniform temperature much more quickly than if it were a solid block two or three feet thick. It is also much lighter, of course; but even so its weight is fifteen and a half tons. If it were a solid block of the same proportions as the 100-inch mirror it would weigh forty tons. It is doubtful whether even the brilliant engineers and technicians who have produced the 200-inch could cope with a mirror weighing forty tons.

The telescope is on such a huge scale that the structure which carries the secondary mirrors and the photographic plate at the primary focus, supported in the middle of the tube at its upper end, serves as a housing for the observer, who actually 'goes for a ride' in the telescope itself. He is in constant telephonic communication with the operator who controls the instrument and can instruct him to point the telescope to any object which he wishes to photograph. The plate is held in a carrier which can be moved in all directions by means of screws, so that the observer can keep the image in focus and make compensating adjustments for any slight errors in the drive of the telescope.

The building housing this colossus is nearly one hundred and forty feet in diameter and is capped by a hemispherical dome which can be rotated on circular rails by electric motors. A wide opening in the side of the dome, extending up to and beyond the top, is closed by motor-driven shutters which can be rolled outwards, rather like the double doors of a tube train, to allow the telescope to peer out at the sky.

Mount Palomar is 5,500 feet high, well above low-lying fog, mist and haze. It is in a region where the sky is brilliantly clear most of the time and where the air is usually steady and homogeneous, with a minimum of the wavering, flickering effects of contending air-currents which make astronomical observations so exasperating in less favoured parts of the world.

No effort has been spared to make this telescope as perfectly fitted for its purpose as is humanly possible. There can be no doubt that it will enlarge our knowledge of the universe, but it certainly will not reach finality.

Every time a great advance in telescopic power has been made, problems have been solved and unexpected discoveries have been made. Every time, also, these discoveries have presented further problems which have had to wait for their solution until a still larger telescope could be made.

We may expect that before many years have elapsed astronomers will be calling for a telescope of 300 inches aperture to supply the answer to questions raised by the observations made with the 200-inch. Such an increase in size would no doubt present many difficult problems, but so did Galileo's first telescope, Herschel's 4-foot reflector, Lord Rosse's 6-foot, the 60-inch, the Victoria 72-inch and the 100-inch.

The 200-inch is so huge that it is impossible to take a photograph of it which shows it clearly in its entirety. Plate XVI is a photograph of a one-tenth scale model of it, which (apart from a few minor details) represents the 200-inch as it would be seen from an aeroplane flying past the opening in the dome at a height of about 130 feet from the ground. The 'tube' of the telescope is the skeleton-like structure in the middle.

Plate XVII gives a vivid impression of the size of the mirror. The surface of the mirror occupies the foreground of the picture. The circle a little to the right of the centre is the outline of the central hole, filled in by a temporary glass plug to facilitate the optical work. The three men are sitting on a polishing tool six feet in diameter which is lying in a patch of rouge and water on the surface of the mirror. They are not sitting there for fun; they are using their weight to assist in moulding the layer of pitch on the underside of the polishing tool so that it shall be in perfect contact everywhere with the optical surface.

CHAPTER XI

IS THE UNIVERSE FINITE OR INFINITE?

MOST people at some time or other have wondered about infinite space. We imagine ourselves moving outwards in a straight line, out among the stars and beyond them. Can we go on literally for ever? Is there an end – a boundary or barrier? If so, what is beyond it? We are defeated; our minds are not capable of comprehending boundless infinity.

At a time when the size of the galactic system was unknown it was possible to imagine that however far we went in any direction we should still find ourselves surrounded by stars. Against this, it was argued that if space is boundless and infinite and the stars are infinite in number, nowhere coming to an end or thinning out, then we should see no dark spaces between the stars; the whole sky would be a blaze of light. We know now that the stars (our stars) are not infinite in number and that a journey at the speed of light would in a few thousand years take us right outside the swarm of stars which is the galactic system. The darkness of the night sky is therefore satisfactorily explained.

Now, however, the same question arises on a much vaster scale. There are many millions of such swarms and our largest telescope does not penetrate to the limit of the swarm of swarms. If the nebulæ go on for ever, why do we not see the whole sky uniformly bright all over?

There is one answer to this question which seems to be plausible if the red-shifts are really due to recession. At 500,000,000 light-years' distance the recession is nearly one third of the velocity of light. If the simple proportionality between distance and velocity of recession holds for all distances, however great, the recession will reach the velocity of light at a distance of about 1,750,000,000 light-years. A nebula at that distance, therefore, will be invisible because its light, emitted at a speed equal to the speed at which it is moving away from us (or we away from it) will never reach us. There is a limit, therefore, to the number of nebulæ that can be seen.

This must be looked at a little more closely. The assumption is that the distance that light travels from its source in a given time is a distance measured from that source, as would be the case if light behaved like shells shot from a gun. It does not behave in that way, however; it is not by any means as simple as that. It is not even as simple as the sound-waves from the whistle that were dealt with in Chapter 5.

We know how sound-waves travel; there is no mystery about them at all. As soon as the sound has left the whistle it propagates itself through the air by a kind of wave motion. The air is alternately compressed and rarefied. This wave motion is a matter that concerns the air and nothing else – not even the whistle. The speed at which the waves travel has nothing to do with the speed at which the whistle is travelling, or the speed at which the hearer is travelling. We say that the speed of sound is constant relative to the air.

Light is pictured as a wave motion of some sort, and this wave motion must (so the argument used to run) take place in something; there must be a medium to vibrate and so transmit light. The name given to this unobservable, impalpable and hypothetical medium was the 'luminiferous ether' – the light-carrying ether.

Clerk-Maxwell, a nineteenth-century mathematician, showed that the properties of light could be accounted for satisfactorily on the assumption that the wave motion is electromagnetic in character. From the known properties of electricity and magnetism he showed that there ought to be such wave motion and that its velocity ought to have a definite relation to certain of the constants of electromagnetic theory. Thus, mathematics was able not only to account for the propagation of light but also, by implication, to predict man-made electromagnetic waves – what we know as wireless or radio. It was Clerk-Maxwell's work that led experimenters such as Hertz, Lodge and Marconi to undertake their pioneer work in this field. It was Hertz who first detected at a distance the waves or radiation from an electric spark. It is very unlikely that he would have done so if the possibility of such a thing had not been made clear by Clerk-Maxwell. We usually think of Marconi as the originator of wireless. We should look back a little further, to James Clerk-Maxwell, who saw it afar off in his equations. There could be no more emphatic proof of a theory.

Wireless waves, radiant heat, light, ultra-violet, X rays, the 'rays' given off by radio-active substances, the 'rays' which killed the inhabitants of Hiroshima and Nagasaki, are all the same, in the sense that the notes in the musical scale are the same. They differ only in frequency and wavelength. They are referred to collectively as *radiation*. All space is filled with it. The physical universe, in fact, consists of matter and radiation.

Now if radiation is a wave motion in the ether, its velocity relative to the ether should be constant, just as the velocity of sound is constant relative to the medium which carries it – the air.

It is not even as simple as that, for observations and experiments show that the velocity of radiation is constant relative to anyone who observes it. However, one thing is quite certain; it is not constant relative to the body which emits the light. If it were, our observations of binary stars, for example, would be very different from what they are.

No, the argument that the light from a nebula 1,750,000,000 light-years away would never reach us is wrong. It *would* reach us in that number of years; but in what form? The answer is that its frequency would be zero and its wavelength infinite. It would not be radiation at all; we could not see or photograph the nebula by its aid, nor become aware of it in any other way. In a word, the nebula would be unobservable. This is as much as to say that it would not exist so far as we are concerned.

Some readers may regard this as quibbling; but that would be a short-sighted view, for this reason. In calculating the rise or fall of pitch of the sound of the whistle heard by the man on the platform (Chapter 5), we relied on the constancy of the velocity of sound relative to the air – and we also assumed that there was no wind (although we did not say so at the time), thereby making the velocity of the sound constant relative to the hearer. So also, in calculating the velocity of recession of a nebula from the red-shift, we assume the constancy of the velocity of light, not relative to the nebula but relative to the observer. Before 1905 (when Einstein published his papers on the Special Theory of Relativity) we should have said 'relative to the ether' – and we should have assumed, either explicitly or implicitly, that the ether wind was not blowing. We now have good reason to believe that there is no such thing as an ether-wind nor, in fact, any ether at all. This will be explained a little later, under the heading 'Relativity'.

What of a nebula at a distance of 1,751,000,001 light-years? The only answer that can be given at this stage (on the assumptions so far made) is that it would be unobservable. A different answer can be given on other assumptions, as will (we hope) be made clear later. Taking the earth's circumference to be 24,000 miles, a place 12,001 miles from Burlington House is also 11,999 miles from Burlington House.

We are now getting into deep water. The mere mention of Einstein's name will have told the reader this, apart from anything else. We shall have to tackle him sooner or later if we are to make any headway in understanding the nature of the universe, but in the meantime we can sum up the argument, as far as it has gone, in this way. If the frequency-distance relation holds throughout the universe, if the red-shifts are the Döppler effect, indicating real motion of recession, and if space is straightforward, with no Einstein twists or kinks in it, then nebulæ at distances of 1,750,000,000 light years or so, and beyond, are unobservable and in a sense can be said to be non-existent; for science does not concern itself with things that cannot be observed in fact or in principle. We can assume that there are nebulæ beyond the obscuring clouds of the Galaxy, because we can imagine these clouds moving out of the way. We cannot assume that there are nebulæ beyond the limit set by the velocity of light, because we cannot imagine the velocity of light, or the consequences of its properties, being other than what they are.

Now let us assume that the nebulæ on the whole are stationary and that the red-shifts are due to some cause other than the Döppler effect. The answer is the same; at the limit of 1,750,000,000 light-years the shift would become so great that the spectrum would vanish altogether. There would be no receivable or detectable radiation. Nebulæ at and beyond that distance would not be observable at all. In the sense explained above, they do not exist.

The next question that must be examined is how the red-shifts could arise if they are not due to motion. The frequency of the light at any point in the spectrum (the K line of calcium for example) is a natural frequency of the atoms concerned – calcium atoms in the case of the K line. This natural frequency can be thought of as an extremely rapid vibration within the atoms. We know that on the earth these various frequencies are very stable. Certain agencies (pressure, for example) can affect them, but the amount by which they are affected is known and can be allowed for.

We have, however, been observing and measuring them only for a very short time. We cannot therefore deny the possibility that these natural frequencies of the atoms may change with the passage of time. If nature is such that the inherent, natural frequencies of the atoms increase uniformly with time, the red-shifts are fully accounted for and they supply a measure of the rate at which the increase takes place. This is clear because the light by which we observe the nebulæ left them a very long time ago, when (we assume) the frequencies were smaller than they are now. We are, in a particular case, comparing calcium atoms on the earth now, with calcium atoms in a nebula one hundred million years ago; and we should not assume that the two sets of atoms have the same properties.

Incidentally, this last sentence illustrates the inadequacy of language in the face of these questions. The present tense 'have' is used in connection with things now and things

100,000,000 years ago. It is difficult to see how otherwise the thought can be expressed equally succinctly.

What of the nebula 1,750,000,000 light-years distant? Its atoms 1,750,000,000 years ago were vibrating at a frequency of zero – actually, and not apparently as on the Döppler assumption – which of course means that they were not vibrating at all. Non-vibrating atoms are unobservable. The answer is the same as on the Döppler assumption. It is doubtful whether an atom having zero frequency can be said to exist in any sense whatever. If atoms 1,750,000,000 years ago were non-existent, are we justified in saying that the universe came into existence that number of years ago?

Another way of accounting for the red-shifts is to assume that radiation loses energy during its passage through space. There is no reason to suppose that it does, but the red-shifts are so remarkable that any possible explanation, whatever other questions it may raise, must be examined. The properties of radiation are such that we are forced to assume that, like matter, it is discontinuous or atomic. The 'atom' of radiation is called a quantum, and it is a quantum of energy. The amount of energy in a quantum depends on its frequency. In fact, if we divide the energy of any quantum by its frequency the quotient or ratio is constant.

Now if the quanta, during their journey through space, lose energy progressively, the frequency must diminish progressively in the same proportion in order that the ratio of energy to frequency shall remain constant. Hence the necessary consequence of a loss of energy of the quanta of radiation is a shift of the spectrum lines towards the low-frequency (red) end of the spectrum.

A nebula 1,750,000,000 light-years away, on this theory, sent out normal light in the normal way, but when it reaches us it has lost all its energy and therefore its frequency is zero. The light has petered out and we have no means of becoming aware of the existence of such a nebula, or of any nebulæ there may be still further away. It, and they, do not exist so far as we are concerned.

Whichever way we consider the matter, therefore, the result is the same; the red-shift implies that the number of nebulæ that we can be aware of by any means whatever is limited.

We can now give another answer to the question, 'what is the size of the universe?' It is not more than 3,500,000,000 light-years in diameter; or if it is, we can never become aware of the fact.

WHY ARE THE NEBULÆ RECEDING – IF THEY ARE?

If we assume that the nebulæ are receding, or rather spreading apart, we must ask how such a motion could originate. The simplest explanation of all is what may be called the 'shell-splinter' theory. When a shell bursts, various fragments are propelled outwards in various directions at various speeds. They are slowed down by the resistance of the air and their tracks are deflected by the earth's attraction (to use the language of Newton). But we can easily imagine a shell bursting in outer space, a long way away from any planet or star. In such circumstances each fragment would continue to move in a straight line at the speed with which it set out, there being nothing to retard it and nothing to deflect it.

Quite obviously, after a certain time those which are moving very fast will be found a long way away from the point where the burst took place, while those which are moving more slowly will not be so far away. If there are a great many fragments and if their speeds are suitably distributed (not too high a proportion moving at any one speed), the result after a time will be a roughly globular swarm of particles *spreading apart*. If each one carried an observer, each observer would conclude that all the other particles were moving away from him, but on reflection he would see that this is only half the truth. They are moving away from one another.

Thus, on this theory, all the matter in the universe was at one time concentrated in a small space. About 2,000,000,000 years ago something happened which caused various parts of it to move outwards at various speeds, possibly up to and including the speed of light. Now, after 2,000,000,000 years, we see the result; the various parts have spread apart and, quite naturally, those that have travelled faster have gone further.

It is claimed for this explanation that it does not call for acceleration of the nebulæ; they have always been moving at the same speed since the catastrophic beginning of their flight. If they were constantly increasing their speed, there is the great difficulty that some sort of force (a kind of negative or inverted force of gravity) would be required to cause the acceleration. But the difficulty is still there; they were initially at rest, and then were moving (some of them) at enormous speeds. The forces required to accelerate them in a relatively short time would be unimaginably great. We can only think dimly of some kind of gigantic nuclear explosion – Hiroshima multiplied by a factor of millions of millions.

If the present state of the universe originated in some such catastrophe, its state before the catastrophe must have been utterly different from anything we can imagine. If the universe can be said to have had a beginning, then this catastrophe was the beginning – if the theory is correct.

RELATIVITY

We can put it off no longer; we must take the plunge into this formidable but fascinating subject, or rather into the ideas which underlie the mathematical theory. The mathematics is exceedingly difficult, but the ideas on which it is based are not at all difficult to grasp.

Let us first consider the propagation of light through space. If there is a medium (the ether) which by vibrating transmits light from place to place, then when we say that light travels at 186,000 miles per second we mean 186,000 miles through the ether – from one identifiable piece of ether to another identifiable piece 186,000 miles away.

We can easily make 'pieces' of air identifiable, for example by floating free balloons in it or releasing puffs of smoke. We can then time the sound as it travels from one balloon or puff of smoke to another. This is the principle; in practice we simply choose a windless day for the measurement or do it in a closed space.

We cannot identify different parts of the ether in any such way. When we measure the velocity of light as it travels from Jupiter to the earth (in Roemer's observations) or between two fixed points on the earth, we are rather in the position of a man trying to measure the speed of sound between two points on the earth while neglecting to notice whether there is a wind blowing or not.

Suppose we had no means of detecting wind except by measuring the velocity of sound in various directions. Two people, armed with synchronised watches, could station themselves a mile apart, first north and south, then east and west, and so on, and measure the speed of sound in those various directions, one of them firing a pistol at an agreed instant and the other timing the sound of the shot. They could soon find out the direction and speed of the wind in that way.

What of a man obliged to work single-handed? All he could do would be to set up a reflecting screen at a known distance in various directions, fire pistol shots and time the echoes. The time taken for the sound to travel to and from the reflecting screen is greater in the direction in which the wind is blowing than it is across wind. He could therefore tell whether the wind was blowing along the north-south line or the east-west line; but he would be unable to distinguish between a north wind and a south wind, or between a west wind and an east wind.

In our dealings with light we are like this single observer. If the ether is blowing past us (or if we are moving through it, which is the same thing) we have no knowledge of it; we cannot feel an ether wind. When we wish to measure the velocity of light (otherwise than by Roemer's method) we have to send the light on to a mirror and time its return – the echo.

Now we have no direct knowledge of any movement of the ether relative to the solar system or relative to the galactic system. We do know, however, that in June we are moving towards a particular star and in December we are moving away from that star. This was confirmed, as was explained earlier, by Bradley's discovery of aberration.

If therefore we wish to detect an ether wind, we must make use of this fact, because whatever the speed and direction of this wind, it will be greater at one time of the year and less six months later, by reason of our movement round the sun. We therefore adopt a procedure similar to that of the single-handed observer who wished to find the speed of the wind by measuring the velocity of sound; we measure the velocity of light in the direction of the orbital movement of the earth and also in a direction at right-angles to it, repeating the measurements at different times of the year. If light is carried by an ether in the same way that sound is carried by the air, some time in such a series of experiments a difference of velocity will be detected.

Michelson and Morley, two American physicists, first performed this experiment in 1887 with apparatus fully capable of detecting the expected difference. None was found; the velocity of light was the same in all directions at all times. The experiment (always referred to as the Michelson-Morley experiment) has been repeated many times since then, always with the same result. The velocity of light, going from the observer to a mirror and back again, is always the same in all directions.

Many suggestions were made to account for this. One was that the ether near the earth was dragged along with it; but if this were so, grave difficulties would arise in connection with the aberration of light and in other connections. Another suggestion was that material bodies, including the apparatus used by Michelson and Morley, become shorter in the direction of their movement through the ether, the shortening being of just the right amount to compensate for the longer time that light takes to travel to and fro in that direction (up and down wind), than in the direction at right angles, or across wind.

Einstein showed that the whole question was resolved – disappeared, in fact – if we simply accepted the result of the Michelson-Morley experiment. We had asked a question of nature and we had been given the answer: the speed of light is constant relative to the observer. Consequently there is no ether; for if there were, the answer would have been different.

This view of the matter simplifies things very greatly. Some of its logical consequences seem very paradoxical, but we need not concern ourselves with them. Our main interest in this 'special' theory of relativity is that it justifies our assumption that the light from all the nebulæ reaches us at a constant velocity and that our conclusions based on the red-shifts are correct.

We now have to follow Einstein into his 'general' theory and in particular the explanation of gravitation that it provides.

Newton's great generalisation was based on the observed fact that material bodies tend to move towards one another. To account for this tendency he introduced the idea of a force, similar to the force that we exert with our muscles, but acting at a distance through empty space. He made assumptions about space (it was in accordance everywhere with the geometry of Euclid) and about time (it flowed uniformly and continuously and was independent of space) which seem so reasonable and have been so generally accepted that the fact that they were only assumptions came to be overlooked.

The idea underlying the Einstein view of the matter may be stated thus: We can account for gravitation, even more accurately than Newton did, by rejecting the idea of a force acting at a distance and by ridding our minds of assumptions about the nature of space and time. If we do these things, and accept the results of experiment and observation without question, we can construct a self-consistent picture of the universe in which space, time, radiation and material particles are all intimately linked with one another and in which the motions of the planets, of a stone thrown or dropped from the hand, of the stars and the nebulæ, are the consequence not of forces acting at a distance but of variations in the geometrical nature of space associated with material particles.

Newton insisted on a particular kind of space and time, in which material particles left to themselves would move uniformly in straight lines. To account for the fact that material particles do nothing of the sort, but move in curved paths with varying speed, he had to introduce the force of gravitation, acting across empty space in a way which neither he nor anyone else could explain.

Einstein makes no assumptions about space; to begin with he knows nothing about it at all. He observes the various curved paths pursued by stones, planets, comets and other bodies and their variations of speed and, assuming that these movements are in the natural order of things, he enquires what are the properties of space and time that would make such movements natural and inevitable. His mathematical equations give the answer. They account completely and naturally for certain observed facts which cannot be accounted for by Newton's laws. On this account alone Einstein's ideas must be preferred to Newton's, just as the Copernican scheme had to be accepted and that of Ptolemy rejected.

It is true that the observed facts mentioned above can be explained on Newtonian principles by making further assumptions, just as the Ptolemaic system could be adjusted to fit the observations by adding more and more circles to the original scheme shown in Figure 5. The Copernican system was preferred because it did not need any such patching (after it had been perfected by Kepler), and we now have to make the same choice between Newton and Einstein.

In the solar system, and even in the galactic system, the differences between the motions of material bodies according to Newton and according to Einstein are exceedingly small. Among the planets, only one (Mercury) shows a definite preference, unmistakably favouring Einstein.

This matter of Mercury can be disposed of in a few words. The orbit of Mercury is elliptical, and one particular point on that orbit is nearer to the sun than any other point. This is the point of perihelion. If Mercury were the only planet revolving round the sun, this point would always be in the same position, according to Newton. The perturbations of Mercury by the other planets cause the perihelion point to move slowly round the orbit, and this effect can be calculated with precision. The observed movement of the point of perihelion, however, does not agree with the Newtonian calculations and all attempts to explain the discrepancy on Newtonian lines have failed.

According to the Einstein theory, however, the perihelion point would move round the orbit even if Mercury were the only planet. When the effect of perturbations is added, the result agrees perfectly with the observations.

We will pass over another of Einstein's predictions (a redshift of small amount caused by gravitation) because it has no direct bearing on our theme.

The third of the Einstein predictions received a great deal of publicity in the press some years ago when headlines such as 'Light Caught Bending' and 'Kink In Space' were to be seen. The prediction was that light passing close to the sun would be deviated slightly from its straight course. During an eclipse of the sun, stars near the sun's limb were photographed and found to be slightly out of position, just as they would be if their light, in passing close to the sun, had been deflected a trifle towards the sun.

The point of this is that according to Newton's theory there is no reason whatever to imagine that light is affected by the force of gravity. It can, of course, be *assumed* that it is, and the amount of the deflection can then be calculated. In Einstein's theory, however, light *must* pursue a curved path in passing close to the sun. It is inevitable; it follows directly from the theory and requires no additional assumptions of any kind.

Moreover, this Einstein deflection is twice the amount that it would be if Newton's scheme were correct and if the additional assumption were made (quite arbitrarily) that light is affected by the force of gravity.

The observations of the deflection are very difficult and at present it cannot be said with certainty that the *amount* of deflection observed favours Einstein. The fact that there is any deflection at all, however, clearly favours the later theory because such deflection is a necessary consequence of that theory, but not of Newton's theory.

Einstein's conception of gravitation can best be understood by considering experiments performed in a lift-cage under various conditions. Some of these conditions could not at present be reproduced in practice, but they are not impossible in principle. No-one is in any doubt about the truth of Einstein's account of the happenings in this lift-cage, although it is open to anyone to disagree with him about the significance of them.

Ordinary experience in lifts is somewhat restricted in scope. Before the lift starts we experience no unusual sensation. When it begins to go up we have a momentary sensation of increased weight. Just before it stops at an upper floor we feel momentarily lighter. If the lift is going down these sensations are reversed; we feel lighter for a moment as it starts and heavier for a moment as it stops.

If the cable were to break and the safety devices were to fail, we should feel very light indeed during the descent – in fact we should weigh nothing at all. The floor would not be pressing upwards on our feet, nor our feet pressing downwards on the floor. If we let go of something it would not fall; it would appear to stay in mid-air. If we threw it across the lift it would travel in a straight line. Our loss of weight during the descent would be amply compensated by a very great increase of weight at the bottom; but experiments during that phase would scarcely be possible.

Einstein asserts (and no-one can contradict him) that all the relevant conditions in this falling lift are identical with those that would obtain in the lift if it were out in empty space, remote from the earth or stars. There, the Newtonian force of gravity is absent. Nothing falls, things thrown move in straight lines, our feet do not continually press against anything nor does anything press against them. Einstein invites us to accept this and all its implications.

Going further, we now fit our interstellar lift with rockets, so that we can accelerate it upwards at the same rate as bodies fall on the earth. A body falling freely increases its speed by about thirty-two feet per second every second. We adjust our rockets so that our speed increases by thirty-two feet per second every second. The floor now presses on our feet in the familiar way (we say that our feet press on the floor), if we let go of an object it falls to the floor, and if we throw it across the lift it describes a curved path, appearing to us to accelerate downwards (in both cases) just as it does on the earth. The moment we let go of it, it ceases to be propelled by the rockets; it simply stays behind.

No dynamical experiment that we can perform in this lift, under these conditions, will give a result in the slightest degree different from that which it gives in the stationary lift on the earth. Einstein again invites us to accept this conclusion and all its implications.

Among these implications is this: in our rocket-propelled lift, a ray of light passing across the lift from outside will be deflected downwards. This is so because during the passage of the ray from side to side the lift will have accelerated upwards slightly. This deflection is a natural and inevitable consequence of the acceleration of the lift, as was the downward acceleration of the object which we let 'fall'.

Because we cannot distinguish between the conditions in the rocket-propelled lift and in the stationary lift on the earth, we are to accept the conclusion that they are identical. The earth, apparently pulling us downwards, giving us the impression of weight, causing things to fall, and so on, is in reality doing nothing of the sort; it has so altered the characteristics of the space surrounding it that we are, in effect, being accelerated upwardly without changing our position. When the lift-cable breaks, the lift and everything in it is (in effect) stationary – until the bottom of the lift-shaft hits it.

Again, owing to our inability to distinguish, we must conclude that a ray of light from outside, passing through the stationary lift on the earth, will be deflected slightly downwards. Of course it is not merely a matter of the lift; the conditions are the same everywhere on the earth and this downward deflection of the ray of light would happen over a wide area. The deflection would be immeasurably small because the acceleration due to the earth's gravity is only thirty-two feet per second per second. The acceleration due to the sun's gravity is very much greater, and a deflection of this kind caused by the sun would be measurable.

Any reader who rejects the conclusions in the last two paragraphs as nonsense should call to mind that it was on the basis of these conclusions that Einstein predicted that light passing close to the sun from a star would be found to be deflected. It *was* found to be deflected. No-one else had made any such prediction as a consequence of any rival theory. Einstein's ideas therefore hold the field.

What has all this to do with the red-shifts and the size of the universe? The conclusions that we reached about the consequences of the red-shift were, it will be remembered, based on the understanding that 'space is straightforward, with no Einstein twists or kinks in it'. What if space is not straightforward?

Space, says Einstein (but we ought really to say 'space-time') is conditioned in its properties by the matter which it contains. The two are not independent. Space is not everywhere the same. The axioms of Euclid are not necessarily true of real space. Applying the theory to a universe consisting of a swarm of nebulæ, the conclusion is that there are several possible configurations, one of which resembles closely that which we observe.

FINITE BUT BOUNDLESS SPACE

At this point let us recall the first paragraph of this chapter, in which we tried to imagine ourselves travelling endlessly through infinite, boundless space. We are now offered an alternative – *finite* but boundless space. This is space which everywhere curves upon itself, so that in time, travelling on what appears to be a straight course (guided by a ray of light, which is the criterion of straightness), we come back to our starting point. We have encountered no boundaries or barriers. We can travel for ever in a 'straight' line (that is, along the track of a ray of light), although after a time (a very long time indeed) we should find our surroundings familiar.

Furthermore, the theory leads to the conclusion that such a universe would not be stable. It would tend to change its dimensions, becoming either smaller or larger progressively. If it is becoming larger, all the objects in it will be spreading apart. That is what we observe – or rather our observations of the red-shifts are consistent with this idea.

Once more, then, we find a consequence of the Einstein system of ideas corresponding with the observations. Everything that we have observed so far in the universe is consistent with its being a finite, boundless, curved continuum, thickly studded with nebulæ, and continually expanding. Its radius of curvature is continually increasing.

We can give analogies which help us to some slight extent to grasp this difficult idea. The earth was at one time thought to be flat, and indeed any area of a few square miles on its surface is to all intents and purposes flat. If we travel long enough in a 'straight line', however (and the best we can do is to travel in a great circle), we arrive back at our starting point. We can then begin all over again if we wish; there are no absolutely impassable barriers. In any case, we can fly above barriers.

The earth, however, is not expanding. If it were, while remaining spherical, its radius (which of course is its radius of curvature) would be continually increasing. Moreover, all points on its surface would be spreading apart uniformly. An observer in London would say that all cities and towns all over the world were becoming continually more distant *from London*, the more distant ones receding more rapidly than those nearer. An observer in New York would say that all cities and towns all over the world were becoming more distant *from New York* – and so on.

It is hard to imagine an expanding earth. We can, however,

all inflate toy balloons. If we make ink spots all over a toy balloon and then inflate it, the ink spots will spread apart as the balloon increases in size and its radius of curvature increases in length. If, instead of ink spots, we apply little patches of paper, firmly stuck on, or spots of hard varnish which will not stretch when dry, we shall find, of course, that these patches or spots do not increase in size, and moreover that as the rubber between them stretches they cause local deformations in the generally spherical curvature of the surface.

These, it is true, are poor analogies but are offered as some small help in trying to imagine the unimaginable. Let us not, however, reject this scheme of the expanding universe (gravitation being merely local 'puckers' or deformations in the continuum) solely because it is unimaginable. Let us remember that the alternative (infinite, boundless space) is also unimaginable.

The red-shifts, the frequency-distance relation, the deflection of light passing the sun – these are strange, portentuous facts. We must expect the final solution, if it is ever forthcoming, to be strange and portentous.

If the universe is expanding, in the sense of this attempted explanation, we cannot say what size it is because its size is continually increasing. We may hope however, to learn in time the rate at which it is expanding and its radius of curvature at a particular epoch. We may hope that when, with the 200-inch telescope, we have explored a volume of space eight times the size of that already surveyed, clues to these questions will be forthcoming.

Readers who wish to pursue this subject beyond the above necessarily brief outline will find it explained more fully and in greater detail in *The Expanding Universe* by the late Sir Arthur Eddington. This, however, was written some years ago (in 1932) and therefore the account that it gives of the observational material is somewhat out of date.

CHAPTER XII

SUMMING-UP

THE reader is now in possession of at least the outlines of the evidence on which our present views of the size of the universe are based, and is able to judge for himself. Some doubts and questions may have arisen as to whether certain of the later conclusions may not have vitiated, or at least called in question, the principles explained in the earlier chapters. For example, we began by assuming that rays of light are straight lines corresponding strictly to the straight lines of our scale diagrams. Later on we find reasons for doubting whether Euclidean geometry applies to actual space as it does to the abstraction defined by Euclid's axioms and postulates, or as it does to lines on a piece of paper. If these doubts are valid – if the views of Einstein and his school are correct – what of the principles with which we began the investigation? Are they still valid, or must we modify them? If modification is necessary, are the conclusions altered materially?

The answer is that the principles are still valid in the system of Einstein as they were in the system of Euclid and Newton. The modification of space which replaces the force of gravity does not disturb the reasoning on which the determination of the distances within the solar system is based. Rays of light which we assumed to be straight are curved, according to Einstein, but the velocity of light is so great in relation to the 'space-bending' powers of the sun and planets that the curvature is quite inappreciable.

Light from a star, however, is deflected appreciably when it passes close to the sun: the deflection has been observed. Presumably similar deflections occur when light passes close to any star other than the sun. Could there be any such effect which might vitiate our measurements of stellar parallax? Here again we can be reassured; there is no such effect. Any such curvature imposed on the light from a star is the same in all positions of the earth in its orbit and the parallactic displacement, due to the earth's motion round the sun, occurs to the same extent whether the path of the light is curved or straight.

What of the general curvature of 'closed' space? This (if it exists) is a property of space as a whole. Within the confines of each individual nebula the curvature is modified (according to Einstein's views) by the material of which it is composed. The 'local' curvatures thus produced are much more pronounced than the general curvature, being analogous to small but steep indentations or puckers in the surface of a large balloon. If they have no effect on our measurements within the galactic system, we can be certain that the very much gentler general curvature has none.

This general curvature would, however, profoundly affect our interpretation of the observations of very distant nebulæ, but up to the present the volume of space that has been surveyed is far too small to provide any observational clue to such curvature. One of the exciting prospects of the next few years is that the 200-inch telescope may reveal clues of this kind.

Another question that may be asked is this. We have confidently interpreted as Döppler effects the shifts of lines in the spectra of stars in the galactic system, and in many cases the motion in the line of sight derived from these shifts has been used to measure distances. If the red-shifts of the nebulæ beyond the local group should prove not to be due to motion in the line of sight, will doubt be cast upon the interpretation of the shifts found within the galactic system?

The answer is that the only reason for doubting that the nebular shifts are due to motion is because they are unlike those found in the galactic system, being very much greater in amount, unidirectional (they are all shifts towards the red) and systematically related to distance. These are the features that may ultimately require an explanation other than that of motion.

They are absent in the relatively minute dimensions of the

galactic system and there is therefore no reason whatever to doubt that the shifts in the spectra of galactic stars are true Döppler effects. This interpretation is well supported by observations of other kinds. There are no discrepancies or anomalies; the distances based on Döppler shifts take their place harmoniously in a self-consistent scheme.

We will now try to make a general survey of the universe so far as it is known to us, pointing out features of special significance.

The uniformity of the universe is perhaps its most striking feature. We recognise ninety-two elements on the earth, from hydrogen to uranium. We have not found all these elements in the sun, stars and nebulæ, but we have found none that we are not familiar with on the earth – none outside the bounds of the ninety-two. These are the constituents of the whole material universe (these and the constituents of their atoms – protons, neutrons and electrons) and so far as we can tell there are no others.

Among the stars of the galactic system the same types are to be found everywhere. A very high proportion of the stars are binaries; possibly the binaries are in the majority. There are, it is true, 'freak' stars which do not belong to recognisable types, but they are relatively few in number. We find stars exactly like the sun everywhere, others exactly like Aldebaran, others exactly like Vega, and so on. This uniformity is really astonishing. It shows itself most significantly in the pulsating stars (the cepheids) which, wherever they are found, display a definite relation between their intrinsic brightness and their period. These stars are certainly constituted 'according to plan'.

The great majority of the stars are composed of hydrogen which is slightly impure – contaminated, as it were, by traces of the other ninety-one elements.

Our galactic system is a swarm of stars like a flattened disc in shape. Around its margin and towards its centre there are opaque and semi-opaque clouds of dust. The whole swarm is permeated by a tenuous cloud of gas. It is rotating as a whole.

The stars are minute specks compared with the average distances between them. Whether there are dark, non-luminous bodies among them in significant numbers we do not know. We know of a few such bodies accompanying one of the millions of G-type dwarfs, but they are so small as to seem utterly without significance. They are composed largely of the impurities mentioned above.

We do not know definitely whether the galactic system is spiral in structure, but as other systems similar to it in many respects are spiral, it is probable that our swarm is spiral also – probably like M 33, but larger.

Next we find that this swarm is one of a small group, possibly consisting of a dozen or so members, among which M 31 and M 33 are conspicuous. The members of this group are on the average about half a million light-years apart.

The uniformity of the universe manifests itself in this local group. The four or five nearest members are found to contain stars, clusters, gaseous nebulæ, all of types familiar to us in our system. Cepheids are found, pulsating with a frequency strictly in accordance with their brightness, obeying the same rule that is followed by their kin here in the galactic system, Novæ flare up and fade away, supernovæ appear at long intervals. Everything is familiar, the pattern is the same everywhere.

Beyond the local group, nebulæ are found thickly scattered throughout the observable region. Most of them are too distant for their contents to be scrutinised in detail, but the similarity between different nebulæ in different parts of the universe is so striking that it is impossible to doubt that they are similar in composition. The same types are found everywhere, endlessly repeated. Plates XI and XVIII illustrate this. These two nebulæ, so similar in general appearance, are in widely different parts of the sky and their distances from us are very different. There are freaks, of course; for example our two companions, the Magellanic Clouds, are shapeless dwarfs. Even the freaks, however, have a certain sameness about them.

Then there are the large clusters which, though separated by vast distances, are remarkably alike not only in their structure and the spacing of their component nebulæ but also in the relative numbers of the different types found in them. Small groups like the one to which our system belongs are found, some of these groups being a great deal more compact than ours.

The average spacing of the nebulæ in relation to their average size is very much closer than that of the stars in the individual nebulæ. The spaces between the stars are many millions of times the diameters of the stars themselves; the spaces between the nebulæ are on the average only a few hundred times their diameters. Even so, light takes on the average about two million years to travel from one to its nearest neighbour.

These flattened swarms of stars are set at all angles, apparently quite at random. They do not, as a whole, display any tendency to set themselves parallel to one another or to pay any like regard to each other. Even in the clusters they appear to be arranged higgledy-piggledy.

On the whole, the large clusters have fewer of the well-developed spirals, such as M 33, than would be expected from the average relative numbers found elsewhere. This fact may ultimately prove to be significant in connection with theories of the origin and development of nebulæ, but at present we can only speculate about it.

The nebulæ range in actual diameter from 1 to about 100. That is to say, the largest are about one hundred times as large as the smallest. If we consider any one type, however, such as the type of which M 31 is an example, the range in size is very much smaller. The range in total brightness of all types is much less than the range in size. In consequence, the small nebulæ in general (excluding irregulars like the Magellanic Clouds) have a much greater 'surface' brightness than the large ones, the total light being concentrated into a much smaller area. This is important from the observer's point of view.

As all photographers know, the surface brightness of an object determines the time of exposure. If there are two nebulæ at the same distance from us, one four times the area of the other but only twice the total brightness, the large one will require twice as long an exposure as the small one, to secure an equally dense image. That is why the spectra showing very large red-shifts are almost all of small, so-called 'early-type' nebulæ. Even with the 100-inch the difficulty of securing spectra of such distant objects is so great that the observers are forced to choose those with the greatest surface brightness.

The full extent of the system of nebulæ is at present unknown. It is certainly much larger than the largest existing telescope can gauge; the 100-inch has not penetrated to its confines. When the 200-inch is in use it will penetrate twice as far as we have so far been able to probe and will explore a volume eight times as great. In addition, it will enable some of the nearer nebulæ to be examined in greater detail and will thereby enable the relation between distance and red shift to be determined with greater accuracy. What more it will tell us we do not know; there may be some surprises in store.

If space is indeed curved and 'closed' – finite but boundless – it is theoretically possible for any object in it to be seen twice. A wireless transmitter on the earth, radiating in all directions, can be received twice. The radiation, following the curvature of the earth by reason of reflection from the ionosphere high up in the atmosphere, reaches a distant receiver by two different great-circle routes. If the receiver is provided with direction-finding devices, its operator will find that the transmitter is bearing south-west, for example, and also northeast. So with light from a luminous object in curved, closed space; it will reach a distant observer by two different routes and will be visible simultaneously in two opposite directions. Our own nebula, the galactic system, may in theory be visible to us as an extremely distant object. It is at the same time the nearest and the most distant object!

There are two provisos to this; firstly, we must have a telescope powerful enough to make such very distant objects visible (or rather photographable) and secondly the rate at which space is expanding (if it is expanding) must not be too great, otherwise the light may not have time to travel round the longer of the two routes.

If the 200-inch were to show us images of two nebulæ exactly alike in every respect and in parts of the sky opposite to one another, then indeed we should have proof that space is curved and closed because the two nebulæ would be one and the same. No doubt identification would be a matter of some uncertainty because one image would be a 'front view' and the other would be a 'back view'. However, there would obviously be not merely one, but a great many such pairs of images, and the evidence would be cumulative.

It is to be feared, however, that nothing of this kind will be found; the radius of curvature of space is probably far too great.

We have found gas and dust in the spaces between the stars. Are they to be found too in the spaces between the nebulæ? So far, no evidence has been detected either of dust or gas. If they exist, they must be exceedingly tenuous or they would give some indication of their presence.

These spaces are by no means empty, however; they contain radiation. The whole of space is tremulous with radiation of various frequencies. We cannot receive all of it here on the earth's surface because a layer of ozone in the upper atmosphere completely absorbs a wide range of frequencies in the ultraviolet. This is a nuisance from the point of view of astronomers and physicists, but perhaps it is just as well, because if it were not for this ozone layer we (including the astronomers and physicists) would all be dead.

Only very recently the first step has been taken to overcome this disability. In America, German 'V2' rockets equipped with spectroscopes have been sent up above the ozone layer and have secured spectrograms of sunlight unscreened by this layer which hitherto has hampered us so severely. No doubt in course of time improvements in this new technique will enable us to extend our knowledge of the radiation which is constantly traversing space in all directions.

Even under the handicap of the ozone layer we have recognised a wide variety of frequencies, from those detectable by wireless receivers to the mysterious 'cosmic rays' which are of extremely high frequency and penetrating power. The investigation of cosmic rays has been proceeding for some years, but the 'wireless' or low-frequency radiation has only recently been detected and investigation of it has barely begun.

Radiation has an odd property; when it arrives after its long journey from the distant nebulæ its frequency is lower than it was when it set out. The change in frequency is greater, the greater the length of the journey. This is a property of the universe as a whole – a universal fact. We cannot yet be dogmatic about its significance.

It is a strange universe that the telescope has revealed to us. Words are wholly powerless to evoke any idea of its scale. To say that it is vast, huge, gigantic, is to understate the case hopelessly. Such words were made for terrestrial use. They are adequate as applied to mountains and oceans, but there are no words to match the system of the nebulæ.

We can grasp the scale of things better by considering the earth in its setting. If we travel in imagination out into space, taking with us the largest telescope yet made, we lose sight of the earth altogether long before we reach the nearest star. When we have travelled one-tenth of the diameter of the galactic system we can still see the sun in our telescope, but if we neglect to keep it in view all the time we shall never be able to find it again. It would be like trying to pick out one particular blade of grass in a field.

When we reach the nearest of the great nebulæ our telescope does not show us the sun at all; we see its surroundings as a faintly glowing mist and we know only that the sun is contributing its minute quota to this glow. By this time we have difficulty in thinking of the earth at all – such a ridiculous little speck.

We have now been cut down to size. We have one further question: if there is any purpose or plan or destiny in the universe, can it possibly have anything to do with us?

THE END

THE BRITISH ASTRONOMICAL
ASSOCIATION

It is remarkable how many people, who have hobbies that they take quite seriously, are unaware of the greatly enhanced pleasure that can be derived from such pastimes, if only they will join one of the societies that have been founded for their benefit, be they philatelists, archæologists, bird-watchers or astronomers.

In Great Britain the two leading astronomical fraternities are The Royal Astronomical Society and The British Astronomical Association. The latter was founded in 1890, its chief objects being to help the *amateur* astronomer to derive greater interest from his hobby, to introduce him to other astronomers and so to guide his activities as to enable him to make contributions of real value to science, even should he possess only a small telescope or none. Membership of the Association is open to everyone interested in astronomy.

The Association publishes ten numbers of its Journal and an Observer's Handbook every year, in addition to which Memoirs are produced from time to time by the various Sections. These Sections, the majority of which are observational, are a special feature of the Association. Each is directed by an expert and is responsible for a programme of co-operative research, in which any member may take an active and useful part. But it is not expected that most of the members will become active observers. For the remainder there are the monthly meetings at Burlington House, W.1, the publications and the feeling of fellowship with other astronomers, with whom it is always possible to get into contact by correspondence if regular attendance at meetings is inconvenient.

The entrance fee is five shillings and the annual subscription one guinea. All those in any way interested in astronomy should write to The Assistant Secretary, 303, Bath Road, Hounslow West, Middlesex, for particulars and nomination forms.

INDEX

PELICAN BOOKS

*Some recent and forthcoming titles
in the Pelican series:*

*A special volume 2s.6d.
†A double volume